VENGEANCE IN THE DEPTHS
The Nuclear Submarine

By Commander George P. Steele, USN

VENGEANCE IN THE DEPTHS
The Nuclear Submarine

SEADRAGON
Northwest Under the Ice

Vengeance

IN THE DEPTHS

THE NUCLEAR SUBMARINE
by Commander George P. Steele, USN

ILLUSTRATED

New York: E. P. DUTTON & CO., INC.

To my children Jane and Jim

ACKNOWLEDGMENTS

THE UNITED STATES NAVY has given me a life of adventure and interesting variety. I am pleased to be able to share with others some of the things I have found so fascinating.

My thanks go to the Submarine Library, Electric Boat Division, General Dynamics Corporation, for many of the illustrations in this book. The United States Naval Photographic Center provided many photographs for which I am grateful.

The painting of the two fighting submarines was done by Kenton Pope, and photographed by Chief Firecontrol Technician John J. Krawczyk, USN.

George P. Steele

The photographs on pages 23, 30, 45, 49, 58, 60, 64, 82, 97, 121, 132, 143, and 157 are courtesy of the General Dynamics Corporation. All other pictures from the United States Naval Photographic Center.

CONTENTS

VENGEANCE IN THE DEPTHS
The Nuclear Submarine

1

SHIPS OF INNER SPACE

TODAY, on this earth, there exist spaceships such as men have dreamed of for generations. They cruise deep inside the oceans that cover more than sixty per cent of the earth's surface and have an average depth of 12,451 feet. Perfectly balanced against the force of gravity, these underwater space craft, or submarines, powered by nuclear reactors, are new masters of our watery "inner space."

Like outer-spaceships of the future, modern submarines are totally isolated from their environment; yet they can communicate with their bases. The depths of the sea are not a natural habitat for human beings. The weight of the water above presses down on the submerged submarine with a terrific force. A rupture of the hull would bring swift death.

But this danger is usually far from the thought of the crews who live comfortably inside the hull, breathing oxygen generated from sea water, drinking water distilled by nuclear energy, and eating special, delicious food.

Only when the boned, condensed rations run low must the submarine return to port. One day soon it may even be possible to grow nutritious food on board, and then the submarine will be able to remain hidden below the waves indefinitely—like Captain Nemo's *Nautilus* in Jules Verne's *20,000 Leagues Under the Sea*. New as all this is, the submarine itself has a long history.

About 1620, Cornelius Van Drebel, serving in the English Navy of King James I, constructed a rowboat covered over with leather and tallow which actually submerged a number of times to a reported depth of 15 feet. It was large enough to carry sufficient air for several hours and was propelled by a dozen brave oarsmen whose oars projected through watertight leather sockets. The story goes that the boat traveled for several miles from Westminster to Greenwich under the Thames, and that the king himself was on board for a trial run.

Another early experimenter was de Son, a Frenchman, who in 1654 equipped an undersea craft with a hand-propelled paddle wheel. But the fantastic claims he made for it caused him to be labeled a charlatan, and nothing came of his efforts.

As early as 1648, Bishop John Wilkins of Chester had forecast the ultimate use of the submarine. He wrote that these devices could "undermine" a warship and help win mastery of the sea.

It remained for Americans to make the first attempt at such a feat more than a century later. It was an act of desperation.

During the American Revolution the tiny navy of the Continental Congress was able only to harass the

far superior British fleet. Because they had control of
the sea the British could move men and supplies
quickly to a threatened point; in this control lay their
hope of quelling the revolt of the Colonies. How could
they be thwarted?

David Bushnell, a Connecticut Yankee, thought he
knew. Fashioning a wooden contraption large enough
to hold a man, he installed in it a corkscrew propeller
which was hand-powered. The bottom of the *Turtle*,
as he named the strange egg-shaped craft, was lead-
ballasted to keep her upright and had a valve which
admitted water under the operator's seat to make her
sink. Then, by using a handpump, the water could
be forced out for a return to the surface. The natural
air supply was good for about a half-hour. Time
enough, Bushnell hoped, to enable the operator to
fasten a big can of gunpowder to the bottom of a British man-of-war and escape before the fuse set off the
charge. One night in September 1776, the *Turtle*, her
time fuse set, began the first submarine attack in history. A brave soldier named Lee actually got her to
the *Eagle*, a British frigate, and began trying to bore
an auger bit into the ship's hull.

But the bit, to which the 150 pounds of gunpowder
was tied, would not go in. The Royal Navy had copper
sheet on the bottom of many of their ships as a protection against fouling sea growths and barnacles
which slowed down the wooden ships. The bit could
not pierce that copper.

After what must have seemed an eternity, Lee jet-
tisoned the explosive before it could blow him up

and worked his craft clear. The can of gunpowder drifted off, and the explosion gave the British only a good scare.

Later attempts by the *Turtle* to get into position to plant a mine were also unsuccessful.

In 1800 Robert Fulton continued the American submarine tradition. He designed a submarine he called the *Nautilus* which he tried unsuccessfully to sell to Napoleon. Then he tried to interest the British Admiralty in the craft, and they let him arrange a test. Fulton blew up a bridge in the Thames, and William Pitt, the Prime Minister, was ready to support him. But the crusty old seadog, Earl St. Vincent, the First Sea Lord, spoke the epitaph. With England still rejoicing over the recent victory of Trafalgar, he said, "Pitt is the greatest fool in creation to encourage a mode of war which those who command the sea do not want, and which, if successful, would deprive them of it."

But the idea of a submarine would not stay dead. In various countries men toyed with it, yet the authorities refused to take the submarine seriously. A Bavarian named Bauer built a submarine in 1850 which dived and failed to surface. The Prussian government refused him money with the words, "If successful it will render all surface navigation impossible." It was a prophecy that in later years proved too accurate for comfort.

The first successful sinking of a warship by submarine action is supposed to have occurred during the American Civil War, though at the cost of the submarine. This is erroneous. It is true that the Confederate Navy's *Hunley* sank the fine new Federal vessel *Housatonic* on February 17, 1864. The tiny submarine was swamped by the water rushing into her opened hatch from the force of the explosion and went down with her entire crew of nine. But the *Hunley* was not operating as a submarine. She had previously sunk three times with all hands, trying to be a submarine, and was now being operated as a "David," as low-riding torpedo boats were called by the Confederate Navy. Later efforts to use submarines in the Civil War were all unsuccessful.

Again a period of experimentation followed. All of the major sea powers now began to listen to the inventors. A Swede, Nordenfelt; an Englishman, Garret; a Frenchman, De Lorne; and two Americans, Holland and Lake, built submarines which began to take the shape of the undersea craft we know today.

In the ten years before the outbreak of World War I, the submarine matured as an effective weapon of war and was commissioned into the world's fleets. By 1914 Britain had built or was building 97 submarines, France 86, the United States 49, and Germany 45.

The undersea craft was now a fair-sized surface ship of nearly 1,000 tons, propelled on the surface by diesel or gasoline engines at a speed of 14 knots. When submerged it could run on electric storage batteries at a maximum speed of about 7.5 knots for a brief period, but usually ran much slower to conserve the precious battery charge.

The steam-driven torpedo was its principal weapon, though it was often fitted with small guns. The tor-

The USS *Holland,* the first United States Navy submarine, went into service in 1900.

pedoes were fired from four torpedo tubes, which could be reloaded. A periscope was used to navigate at shallow depths and to aim the torpedoes.

The World War I submarine had to surface when its electric batteries were exhausted or its air became foul. But this was acceptable because the submarine only dived just before an attack, which rarely took very long. Dives of more than a few hours were rare, and the boats could stay submerged less than two days. Once back on the surface, the engines turned the electric generators which recharged the batteries.

The German *U-21* was the first submarine operating submerged to score a kill—the victim, HMS *Path-finder,* a British cruiser sunk on September 5, 1914. In the same month *U-9* sank three British cruisers in a single day. To Captain Otto Weddigen fell the ships, *Aboukir, Cressey,* and *Hogue,* with the terrible slaughter of 1,400 men. Naval circles were astounded. But that was just the beginning.

The submarine was now ready to play the role in war that Bishop Wilkins had forecast 266 years earlier.

German submarines slipped into the anchorages of the British fleet and hounded it from place to place until, in 1915, it found sanctuary behind nets and mines in Scapa Flow in the Orkney Islands. The baffled German U-boats now turned to a full-scale assault on merchantment in a blockade of Britain.

By the end of 1916, the sinking of merchantmen had reached more than 350,000 tons a month, or about seven ships a day. Germany now adopted unrestricted submarine warfare. Disregarding the rules of international law that had kept her submarines from attacking neutral ships carrying food and supplies to her enemies, the Germans no longer took the trouble to surface to make sure that the merchant ships they were attacking were those of the enemy.

In April 1917, more than 360 ships were sunk—a ruinous 875,000 tons. It was apparent to all that the German submarine menace had to be defeated promptly, or Britain and France would collapse by the end of the year. Germany had more than 110 submarines at sea, and only two U-boats were destroyed that month. The Allies' shipyards were clogged with damaged ships.

But the U-boat was not to triumph. The Allies began to use the convoy system, in which ships were sailed together under destroyer escort, instead of singly. This brought losses under control and the war at sea was stabilized in favor of the Allies.

But the convoy system could not have been successful without the help of the feverishly working British scientists who discovered how to "see" submarines under water at short range. Sonar was invented in the nick of time. This device, as used by destroyers, hurls forth a burst of sound too high for human ears to hear.

A United States Navy plane attacks a German U-boat during World War II.

If the blast noise hits a submerged submarine nearby, a telltale echo will return to the destroyer. The destroyer then drops explosives (depth charges) that sink toward the submarine and explode at a preset depth. This system saved the day.

Between world wars, attempts were made to outlaw the submarine as a weapon of war. They failed, and the submarine grew larger and more powerful, while keeping essentially the same characteristics.

By 1939 United States Navy submarines had grown to about 1,400 tons with ten torpedo tubes and a length of more than 300 feet. On the surface they made over 20 knots, but submerged they still plodded along at a top speed of 9 knots and could only sustain that speed for less than an hour. At slow speed they could stay submerged for over two days, if pressed. The Germans preferred somewhat smaller submarines which were well designed for their World War II task.

As in World War I, the German submarines again had remarkable success. A British aircraft carrier, HMS *Courageous*, was sunk by *U-29* on September 17, 1939. In October of that year, *U-37* penetrated the protected stronghold of Scapa Flow and sank the mighty battleship *Royal Oak*. This astounding feat by Lieutenant Commander Gunther Prien, German Navy, made him one of the great heroes of naval warfare.

The Allied losses began to mount alarmingly. But this time the convoy system was begun quickly. And although there were some very bad periods, in the end the German and Italian U-boats lost. They sank 2,775 merchant ships—not as many as the 5,235 sinkings of the first World War, but with greater tonnage, 14,-573,000 to 12,185,832 tons.

In the meantime United States submarines were playing a major role in bringing Japan to her knees. They sank 1,113 merchant ships for a total of 5,320,095 tons. In addition, United States submarines sank more than 200 naval ships for a total of 577,626 tons. Japan, faced with starvation, was actually making overtures of peace when the first A-bomb was dropped.

Submarine warfare is not without submarine losses. In World War I the Germans lost 187 U-boats, but in World War II they lost a staggering 781. The Italians lost 85 submarines in World War II, and the United States Navy 52.

The Germans lost, despite their remarkable advances in submarine and torpedo design. U-boats were able to run submerged at speeds of up to 18 knots for brief periods on the battery; and their torpedoes had "ears" to listen to the noises of the target's propellers and to home on them. Some torpedoes even steered scientifically calculated patterns so that if they missed at first, their zigzags and circles were almost sure to result in a hit.

What beat the German submarine was the convoy system, plus the Allied use of radar and aircraft. U-boats could now be spotted at great distances while on the surface or while snorkeling. Surface ship sonar also played an important role.

The snorkel, invented in Holland but perfected by

Long-range submarines such as the USS *Cobia* played a vital role in defeating Japan in World War II.

the Germans, was first used by submarines in World War II. A breathing tube was projected above the surface of the sea to get air to recharge the storage batteries of the diesel engines. An exhaust tube let out the exhaust gas. The submarine was thus able to stay essentially submerged and nearly invisible, sucking air in for crew and engines. But the brief period when the submarine snorkeled to recharge her electric storage battery and to freshen the air meant exposure. And Allied aircraft made the most of that exposure.

American submarines were not fitted with snorkels during World War II. Soon afterward, a program of extensive modernization began. Within ten years, diesel submarines had snorkels, streamlining for greater underwater speed, improved batteries, and torpedoes based upon those used by the Germans during the war. But the revolutionary development of the fifties was not the snorkel but the submarine nuclear reactor that furnished steam for continuous high speed under water without using the large amounts of air needed by the oil-burning engines. But what about the air-breathing sailors on board?

At first large supplies of bottled oxygen were carried by nuclear submarines. These were supplemented by big candles which gave off oxygen when burned. Later oxygen-generating equipment was added. The air was cleaned of unwanted odors and gases by air-revitalization equipment.

At last the submarine was transformed from a mere diving boat, submerging for a few hours or days and frequently needing air for engines and crew, into a self-sufficient spaceship of the ocean. The means used to defeat the German submarines in World War II had to be re-examined. Radar will not work under water, yet the nuclear submarine can stay submerged to make its kills using sonar "eyes and ears" alone. The submarine, which had seemed powerful but controllable at the end of World War II, threatens again as a major sea weapon.

In modern fleets submarines play a large and increasingly important role. The Soviet Union has made the submarine its principal naval arm. She has more than 350 effective submarines of various kinds, including missile-firing types and some powered by nuclear reactors. The United States has more than 110 submarines and a growing percentage of them are propelled by nuclear power. As new nuclear submarines are completed, the old diesel-electric boats are retired. In the near future, 41 American Polaris missile-carrying nuclear submarines and 70 antisubmarine nuclear submarines will be in service.

The colors are hoisted aboard the USS *Nautilus* (SSN-571), the first nuclear submarine, during her commissioning ceremony.

Great Britain has 42 submarines plus one nuclear submarine and is building another nuclear submarine. Communist China has about 31. France has 26. Many other countries have smaller numbers of submarines in their navies.

Besides its two principal missions, *firing missiles tipped with thermonuclear warheads* and *killing other submarines,* the undersea ship can be used in wartime for such things as mine-laying and keeping a steady eye on enemy movements. A submarine placed properly is a lifesaving station for aircraft crews unable to make it home from a mission, as they can abandon their craft nearby. The landing of spies and saboteurs by submarines is a favorite subject of adventure writers. A submarine is at home in any job at sea in which secrecy and silence are required.

Germany used diesel submarines successfully as tankers for refueling other submarines in World War II, and the use of nuclear submarines as tankers is receiving serious study today. Consideration is even being given to building nuclear submarine aircraft carriers, although their construction would be expensive and difficult.

A key peacetime submarine mission is exploration. The opening of the Arctic Ocean by a nuclear submarine has been a wonderful bonus of the novel propulsion plant. Now the exciting possibility of examining the depths of the ocean is becoming a reality as submarines are built to go deeper and deeper.

The bathyscaphe *Trieste,* a heavy-hulled little submarine vehicle, was lowered to the bottom of Marianas

Trench off Guam to a record depth of 35,000 feet in January 1960. If the world's highest mountain was placed upside down there with its base at the surface, it would not come within 6,000 feet of the bottom. We have barely begun these explorations.

But let us now go on board one of our latest nuclear-powered killer submarines.

2

INSIDE A NUCLEAR SUBMARINE

As we walk down the pier to board a nuclear submarine, the first impression we get is that of streamlined silent power. Looming up ahead is a dark-gray sail with large white numerals in clean relief on the side—684; a flipperlike diving plane for ship control submerged projects from each side of the sail. The round, tapered hull is visible just above the pier.

A narrow metal ramp with handrails leads from the pier to the deck of the submarine. Standing on deck to greet us is the captain. The gold braid on the sleeves of his blue uniform and on his blue cap gleams in the sun. Flanking him is an armed sailor, the deck watch, and a lieutenant.

We are led forward along the deck, where the gray-black hull slopes away to the greenish water. The bow is shaped like the end of a giant football. The skipper explains that the designers learned from studying the shape of fish that this is the best kind of streamlining for keeping water resistance to a minimum.

No high prow protects the deck on the surface underway, and a great wash of water flows over it, dashing back against the foot of the sail as though it were

28

a lighthouse on a lonely rock at sea. But this ship, as the fish it resembles, is designed to operate submerged. Once below the surface of the water there is no splashing, foaming turbulence to slow down the submarine. As a result, it goes much faster submerged.

The heavy steel hatch is raised, revealing a circular opening the size of a street manhole. Down a ladder through the hatchway we climb. The cheerfully lighted interior, covered with stainless steel and sheet plastic, and filled with row on row of dark-brown torpedoes, seems much larger than we had expected. Most of the ship is below the water and the sea laps the submarine's sides above our heads.

At the far end of the room a dozen or more paces away are the ends of six 21-inch torpedo tubes. The shiny brass inner doors are closed. But in battle they can be opened in a few moments. Hydraulically powered rams then push torpedoes smoothly and rapidly home into the tubes. Next the inner doors are closed, the tubes are flooded with water, and the pressure within the tubes is equalized with the sea pressure outside. The outer doors opening onto the sea are opened by remote control, and the crew is ready to shoot angry, explosive-laden "fish" at the enemy.

Above and beside the torpedoes are bunks for the sailors. Amazingly, little chrome ashtrays are to be seen here and there. But the skipper assures us that smoking is not dangerous here.

As we look a little anxiously for the fire exit, a sailor remarks with a laugh that the hatch we came through is especially fitted with an escape hatch. In case of an

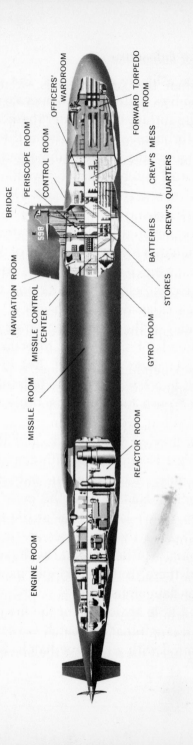

OFFICERS' WARDROOM

FORWARD TORPEDO ROOM

PERISCOPE ROOM

CONTROL ROOM

BRIDGE

CREW'S MESS

CREW'S QUARTERS

BATTERIES

NAVIGATION ROOM

STORES

MISSILE CONTROL CENTER

GYRO ROOM

MISSILE ROOM

REACTOR ROOM

ENGINE ROOM

598

This cutaway of a Polaris submarine has been slightly altered for security reasons.

emergency when the submarine is submerged and cannot surface, the crew is trained to leave the ship one by one through the hatch and float to the surface for rescue. Or if a rescue vessel with a bell is at hand, the bell can be lowered to fit over the hatch. Then the crew rides to the surface inside the diving bell a few at a time without so much as getting wet.

Stepping aft through a narrow oval doorway we pass showers and bathrooms lined with bright metal. The submarine sailors of old were often dirty and unkempt at the end of their brief voyages, but in these new ships life is quite comfortable. Because nuclear submarine crews may stay on patrol for months at a time, it is important that they have comfortable quarters.

Like the deck hatch, this oval door is of thick steel. It swings noiselessly on its hinges and closes with a thud and the click of an engaging latch. A crew member spins the door handle to show us how the "dogs," or "fingers," extend out to grip the rim of metal around the door and hold it fast against pressure. The door protects those in the next compartment or room from flooding water or smoke from a fire.

Opening the door, we step over its high rim into a companionable mess hall where a dozen crew members lounge or work over papers and books at long tables. The bulkheads, or walls, are lined with mementos of the ship's doings, such as plaques given by foreign ships which have been met in foreign ports, framed pictures of famous visitors, and a tablet on which are engraved the names of the first crew. A tele-

vision set is on at the far end of the room, but the
speaker volume is turned off to avoid the commercial
while the men wait for the news. In the meantime
a tape recorder plays a new dance tune.

The captain points out that the mess hall can be
used as an operating room should one of the crew
need emergency treatment. Surgical supplies and
operating-room lights are at hand. But such occasions
are rare indeed, so high are the physical standards for
men on submarine duty.

At the side of the mess hall we look into the shiny
galley. Using the latest electrical appliances, the cooks
are preparing a dinner of southern fried chicken with
all the trimmings. A sailor climbs up from the frozen-
food lockers underneath the deck. Fresh apple pies are
stacked on racks to one side. Next we come to more
living quarters.

The beds in these small bunkrooms are much like
those in the torpedo compartment. Each bunk has an
individual reading light and an individual supply of
cool, purified air which can be adjusted at will. The
bunks look thick and are soft to the touch. Six to eight
men live together in each bunkroom.

The guide takes us up a regular staircase into the
officers' quarters. Here are the little staterooms in
which the ship's officers live two or three to a room.
Each room has a desk and wardrobe, and it is obvious
that every effort has been made to make maximum
use of space. Even the captain's room is tiny, although
he has it to himself. Gay flameproof curtains and bed-

spreads distinguish the wardroom country—as the area is called where the officers live.

The wardroom itself is the size of a small dining room, which is just what it is during meals. But here the officers confer and do paperwork as well. Opposite the captain's seat are instruments that tell him at a glance the ship's speed, course, and depth. Telephones and intercoms give instant communication with vital parts of the ship.

The deck we now tread aft is covered with the same type of vinyl block tile that we have seen elsewhere, but the color is different. The crew chose a color scheme that tastefully matches the deck to the bulkhead paint or plastic. Each compartment has its own color. The skipper informs us that in this way a sense of change and spaciousness is maintained.

While the ship was being built, a committee was formed from those members of the crew living or working in each compartment. Each committee examined the colors and color schemes available in order to come up with a recommendation for the captain. And then the captain reviewed the color schemes to be used in the various parts of the ship. We can see that he has reason to be proud of the result.

A door is now opened into an area of overwhelming complexity. This is the control room, the directing center of the ship. Everywhere are dials, valves, control wheels, indicator lights, and a myriad of strange-looking equipment. It seems impossible for anyone to master it all, but as the host discusses each area in turn,

Equipment is fitted in everywhere possible on a nuclear submarine. The radar is manned on one side of the control room.

the essential order and purpose of the arrangement becomes increasingly clear.

Here, on a raised platform, stands the officer of the deck when the submarine is submerged. He is the watch officer responsible to the captain for the ship and everything she is doing. Usually he has the *conn*, or maneuvering control of her as well. So he has to be able to see instruments indicating where the ship is going.

Before him sit the helmsman and planesman at their stations, holding the controls which resemble steering wheels; their eyes are intent on the panel of instruments in front of them. The helmsman controls the motion of the rudder with the steering wheel, and the planesman moves the steering column before him to position the diving planes on the sail and stern. They regulate the submarine's movement up and down through the water. The officer of the deck, who can easily see the control panel instruments, is able to note any difficulty that the planesman and helmsman might

The diving officer and chief of the watch direct the bow and stern planesmen and the helmsman on the USS *Nautilus*, the first ship to cross the North Pole under the ice.

An officer looks through the retractable periscope of the experimental submarine, USS *Albacore* (AGSS-569).

have keeping the ship at the proper depth and on the proper course. He can then order corrective action.

The OOD can also look at the sonar picture of what is ahead and around the submarine. Sonar is of two types: the kind that picks up the sounds of ships and even fish at great distances, and the kind that makes a loud noise and then picks up the echo as the sound waves are deflected from any object within several miles. Sonarmen are submerged submarine lookouts.

Around the officer of the deck are levers and switches to raise and lower periscopes and radio masts through the sail or to dive and surface the ship. The OOD can report to the captain or talk to any station in the submarine using telephone, intercoms, and general announcing circuits.

At battle stations the captain takes over control of the ship from the officer of the deck, and, from the same raised platform, he can see the instruments that indicate the enemy ship's position and those that are used to fire torpedoes. It is a well-fitted command post.

We are shown past the radio and sonar rooms rather hurriedly because these areas are classified *confidential* or *secret*. Even the ship's crew must stay out of these spaces unless specifically authorized to enter. For in the radio room the top secret messages are encrypted or coded; and in the sonar room are some of the cleverest examples of our electronic art.

There are big covers over the radar and electronic countermeasure devices that detect enemy radar beams, as well as over the depth gauges and speed indicators. The captain explains that the Navy works on a *need-to-know* principle where national secrets are concerned. In spite of having full trust in the crew, the Navy believes it to be unwise to let everyone know everything—a man is told the secrets he has to know to do his job, and no more.

It was fortunate that we had obtained special permission from the Navy Department to go on into the engineering spaces or our tour would have ended at the next doorway. It leads through the reactor compartment. We are hurried on with a promise of a detailed explanation later.

Everywhere in the engineering spaces are pipes great and small, electric motors, control panels, valves and wires, and a glistening steel and plastic appearance is maintained even here where we might have expected grime and oil. The hum and whir of operating equipment is not loud enough to make one raise his voice.

In one corner sailors are working on a salt-water pump. Parts and tools are neatly laid out on a clean cloth. The pump is used to furnish salt water from the sea to cool the air-conditioning sets and the electric generators that power the pump itself, as well as many other units; like organs of the human body, the various items here work for each other and the common good. When one pump needs overhaul, as does this one, alternate or spare pumps take over the work.

It takes at least a year for an officer to get familiar with all of this machinery, and many more years are needed for him to become an expert. The qualification procedures are exceedingly detailed and thorough.

The great engine room houses the main engines that drive the submarine. Here are the generators for electricity to power the lights, ovens, sonars, ventilation fans, and the multitude of other items large and small that operate on electricity, the blood stream of a submarine. To one side of these massive equipments is the maneuvering room.

It is actually not a room at all, but a sort of stall in which the engineer officer of the watch, the reactor operator, and several other key men control the operation of the reactor and propulsion plant as a whole. In front of them, from deck to overhead, is a panel covered with meters, warning lights, switches, knobs, and levers, all laid out in an orderly way. On every side of them these men have telephones and microphones. In case of trouble there is a large general alarm switch to alert everyone on board. The box with all the lights and buttons on it, explains the captain, pointing to a large panel on the bulkhead behind the men on watch, is the temperature-monitoring panel. It watches the temperature of such important items as bearings that give support to heavy rotating machinery. If they overheat, the equipment must be shut down instantly to prevent damage. To demonstrate the panel, the captain touches the alarm, which gives forth a loud honk.

The reactor has many such alarms too, but the best way to prevent trouble is for the men on watch to be perfectly trained, keep alert, and take prompt corrective action.

Squeezing beside the main turbines we move in Indian style to the tapered stern of the submarine and catch a glimpse of a long, round propeller shaft about the size of a big tree trunk in diameter. Although this is as far as we can go, the ship's rudder and stern diving planes add many more feet to the length of the submarine.

For every question that has been answered, there are a dozen more to be asked. So the captain suggests that we come back to the wardroom to discuss how the nuclear reactor is made and the other things that had to be skipped over lightly on our quick walking tour.

3

SUBMARINE NUCLEAR ENGINES

THE NUCLEAR PROPULSION PLANT has revolutionized submarine warfare. But complicated and marvelous though it is, the fundamental ideas on which it is based are really very simple.

A *reactor plant* furnishes steam to the main *propulsion machinery* to turn engines driving the propeller and to the *turbogenerators* that produce electricity for the ship.

Picture a queen ant, surrounded by busy worker ants that feed her and tend to her every need. The reactor is such a queen, surrounded by the plant of worker systems that pump water to cool working parts, remove impurities from her system, and most important, carry off the precious heat that she generates.

For the reactor is just a source of great heat. The heat of nuclear energy replaces the heat of burning oil, coal, or wood that has been used to heat the water to generate steam in boilers of ships since Robert Fulton's successful steamboat of 1807. But on our tour of the ship we saw no fuel storage tanks. On nuclear submarines, the fuel is built in. They need no storage bins or tanks to hold nuclear fuel for the reactor.

Sealed inside a very thick steel pot about the size of an automobile is the uranium fuel, or *reactor core.* Uranium 235 (U 235) gives off heat which is carried away by a tremendous rush of water that flows through the reactor core. The U 235 gives off heat because the centers of atoms are being split.

An atom is the smallest particle of matter that has distinct chemical characteristics. It is so tiny that many billions of them would be needed to make up one dot on this page. However, the uranium 235 atom is a very special kind of atom.

U 235, like the atoms of other elements, has a central mass called a nucleus, with electrons (tiny electrical charges) orbiting it at terrific speeds. But the number of electrons and the number of particles called neutrons and protons that form the central mass of the U 235 atom is much larger than in most atoms.

When a neutron, traveling at the proper speed, hits the big nucleus of the U 235 atom, the nucleus splits apart in what is called fission. Not only are two or more new elements formed by the pieces of the U 235 atom, but heat and radiation result. At least one neutron is driven out at great speed. If it strikes another U 235 atom, the resulting split causes more heat, radiation, and drives out several neutrons. Such a continuing process is called a chain reaction.

The heat is wanted on the submarine to boil water to make steam. And the chain reaction is desirable as long as it is kept under control. A runaway chain reaction in a nuclear reactor would warp or melt the core. An explosion like that of an atomic bomb is impossible with this kind of reactor.

One could do without the radiation, however. Since there is no way to eliminate this by-product of nuclear fission, great care is taken to install thick sheets of lead, plastic, water, steel and the like around the reactor in such a way as to screen out almost all of the radiation. Another way to reduce the effects of radiation is simply not to get close to it. Both the crew and equipment are kept at safe distance from damaging radiation.

An essential rule in nuclear submarines is that no member of the crew may be subjected to more radiation than the tiny amount announced as absolutely safe by the United States Atomic Energy Commission. And the performance of the reactor plants in the service has proved that this standard has been more than met.

How is the reactor turned on and off? Control rods which can be moved by remote control extend through the reactor core. These rods are made of metals such as boron that soak up neutrons. As long as the rods are fully inserted, the chain reaction cannot get started. Most of the neutrons are absorbed by the control rods and fission is stopped.

To start up the reactor, the reactor operator has only to begin slowly to withdraw the control rods. Gradually more and more neutrons cause fission as the rods move out, until as many neutrons are being formed by the fission process as are being absorbed by the control rods or lost into the radiation-shielding. The neutron is so small, and the water, fuel, and steel are so porous that some leak right out of the reactor. When this self-sustaining chain reaction occurs, the reactor is said to be "critical."

The reactor operator can tell what is going on inside the reactor by watching instruments which are sensitive to the number of neutrons escaping from the reactor. The rate of neutron leakage is a good measure of how much fission is going on inside the reactor. The further withdrawal of the rods causes enough fission to heat the water flowing into the core. Once the water is hot, the reactor operator is concerned with keeping the proper amount of fission going.

The water passing through the reactor is under great pressure to prevent it from boiling and turning into steam. Steam does not transfer heat as quickly and evenly from the fuel as does water. The principle here is akin to that of boiling an egg on a mountain top, where the air pressure is lower than at sea level. High on the mountain, the water boils at a lower temperature. With less heat applied, the egg cooks slowly. A pressure cooker would solve the problem by raising the temperature of boiling water, thus speeding up the cooking process.

So in our reactor we simply raise the water pressure very high and let the water passing through the reactor get very hot. Then we can use this extremely hot water to boil water in the boiler at a much lower pressure in the following manner.

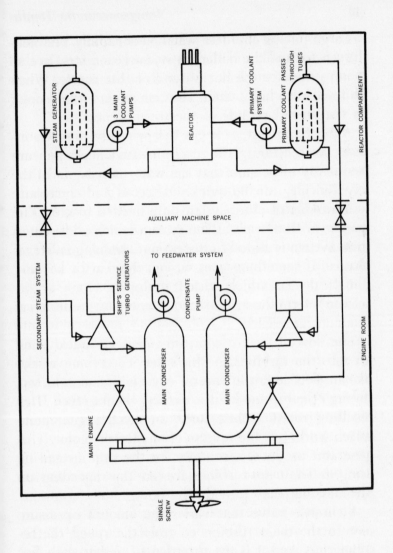

A simplified diagram of the nuclear reactor plant

Large pumps circulate water very rapidly between the reactor and the boilers or steam generators. In the steam generator the hot water from the reactor gives up its heat to boil water. Thus, steam is formed only on the secondary side of the steam generator.

A purifying system keeps the perfectly pure water that courses through the reactor clean. Checks are run frequently to be sure that the water is pure and that any difficulty can be quickly detected and corrected.

A number of other systems are needed to keep the reactor in trim, such as the system which adds water to it. System is added to system until nothing is left to chance. If something goes wrong, the reactor has automatic devices which cause it to stop, or scram, as the scientists term the instantaneous emergency shutdown of a nuclear reactor.

The flow of steam from the steam generator goes aft into the turbines. A ship's service turbine works like an electric fan in reverse—that is, steam is blown through the turbine blades, causing them to turn. The resulting rotation then turns an electric generator, which works just the reverse of an electric motor. The generator produces electricity for the ship instead of using it. The *main* turbines are like the ship's service turbines, but they provide the power for propulsion.

A throttle valve that varies the amount of steam sent to the main turbine controls the speed of the submarine. And it is the throttleman, rather than the reactor operator, who controls the reactor while the ship is steaming underway. There is a valid reason for this.

Assume that the submarine is making half of its designed speed. Suddenly the captain orders full speed, and the throttleman spins open the throttle. More steam is drawn from the boilers which in turn work harder drawing more heat from the water being heated by the reactor. This water becomes slightly cooler as its heat is drained away at a faster rate. Then a wondrous thing happens.

Fission of the U 235 atom nucleus is caused primarily by slower moving neutrons, which none the less move at terrific speeds. Each molecule of water flowing around the fuel plates consists of two hydrogen atoms and one oxygen atom. When the fast-moving neutrons hit the hydrogen atoms they are slowed to a lower speed that is just right for causing fission of U 235.

As we have seen, some neutrons hit nothing and go right on out of the reactor to be finally stopped by the shielding. As the water becomes colder, however, it becomes more dense. More of the fast neutrons are slowed down because the water molecules are closer together. So the rate of fissioning increases and more heat is produced.

The water is then heated again to its normal temperature, expands slightly, and lets extra-fast neutrons escape. Now the increase in the rate of fissioning is stopped. All this happens by merely opening the throttle to draw more steam.

And if the operator closed the throttle completely, the clever reactor would at once react to the resulting expansion of its water because more fast neutrons would then escape collision with hydrogen. And this would reduce the heat output.

The ease and speed with which the nuclear propulsion plant can change its power output is amazing to oldtimers used to oil-fired boilers.

The development of the nuclear reactor took many years, since in science one discovery builds upon another. For example, radioactivity was discovered in 1895 by Wilhelm Roentgen of Germany, who had also discovered the X ray. In 1905, Albert Einstein of Germany gave the world the theory which made radioactivity understandable. Ernest Rutherford of New Zealand first described the atom in 1911.

By 1919 Rutherford had split a proton from a nitrogen atom and other aspects of the atom were discovered, one by one, in succeeding years. In 1938 the uranium atom was split by Otto Hahn and Fritz Strassman in Germany, and the next year the Austrians Lise Meitner and Otto Frisch announced a theory of nuclear fission. The stage was now set for the first nuclear reactor.

On December 2, 1942, at the University of Chicago, the Italian physicist Enrico Fermi and his associates started up the world's first nuclear chain reaction in a pile of graphite blocks into which chunks of uranium had been placed. It was a triumph of science which had immediate results in the production of an atomic bomb and later a nuclear submarine.

Nuclear propulsion for a submarine got its formal start in 1948, when a hard-driving Navy captain (now Vice Admiral), Hyman G. Rickover, was assigned leadership of a group with the task of developing it. Working under the Atomic Energy Commission, as well as the Navy, this brilliant team built a full-scale submarine reactor plant ashore at Arco, Idaho, which

In an unusual role, Dr. Edward Teller (left), "father" of the H-bomb, and Vice Admiral Hyman G. Rickover, USN, "father" of the nuclear submarine, maneuver the USS *Patrick Henry* (SSBN-599), which their work made possible.

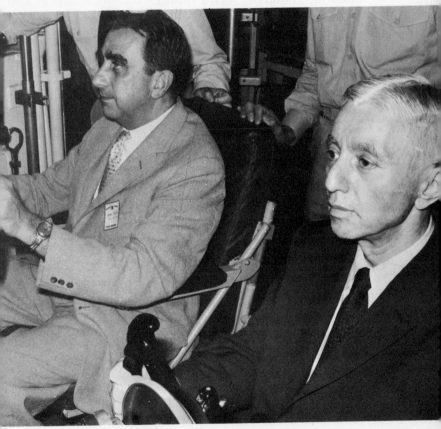

began operation in 1953. The first nuclear submarine, USS *Nautilus,* reported "underway on nuclear power" in January 1955.

The quick pace of modern technology is seen here clearly. In the interval December 1942 to January 1955, slightly over twelve years, the nuclear reactor was developed to the stage where it could be used for propulsion in a warship—a warship that was to shake the foundations of naval power.

To achieve this goal it was necessary to develop new materials and methods. The core of the reactor costs several million dollars. Once it begins operation, the products of its fission are extremely radioactive. These fission products are safe as long as they are kept behind protective shielding and sealed in the core. There can be no repairs to a core at sea.

When the Rickover group began its work, zirconium and other rare metals were not being produced commercially. Metallurgists had to develop ways to obtain at reasonable expense the metals they knew would be needed. Whole new plants were built. Metallurgy was probably the most difficult problem that the scientists and engineers had to solve.

New manufacturing standards had to be set, too. A humble valve such as that used in a plumbing fixture in a house can be made by mass production methods in a soft way. Precision fit is not necessary. If part of the valve wears out after a few years of use, a plumber can easily repair or replace it at a modest cost.

In a nuclear-reactor plant such repair or replacement is far more expensive. It would not do to risk damage to the reactor core through the malfunction of a poorly built valve or other part. It might even cost the lives of the crew if such failures occurred under the Arctic ice or in enemy waters.

At first, manufacturing concerns did not believe that Admiral Rickover would insist on such precision. But they soon found out that the Naval Reactors Organization required near-perfect workmanship for the parts and equipment for reactor plants. In enforcing *hard* methods, the Navy inspectors kept such detailed records that they uncovered even the slightest defects in workmanship and could even tell which workman had made the mistakes.

When the parts arrived at the shipyard for installation, there was no relaxing of vigilance. New inspectors checked everything to see that it was perfect. When a valve was welded into place, the weld was meticulously checked by X ray and other special techniques. One can still check the records on every part of the *Nautilus* reactor plant. While this procedure cannot completely eliminate error, it has played a major role in the remarkable, trouble-free performance of naval reactor plants in the fleet.

Americans who complain about sorry quality in American automobiles, such as mufflers that rust out, ill-fitting doors, and continual mechanical difficulty should realize that tough insistence on performance could restore excellence in manufacture even if it could not bring back pride of craftsmanship. They can vote with their pocketbooks. In the manufacture of naval reactor plants, American industry has proved again that it can do superior work when it is required.

4

COMPLEXITY WITH A PURPOSE

"DIVE! DIVE!" announces the loudspeaker in a matter-of-fact tone, followed by two loud honks on the diving alarm. A loud rush of air and water is heard as the *ballast tanks* are vented and the sea gushes into them. The ship inclines gently downward.

Flooding the ballast tanks, which are spaced along the submarine's hull, gives the ship nearly neutral buoyancy. With perfect neutral buoyancy she should hang motionless, neither rising nor sinking.

To allow for changes in the amount of stores, ammunition, water, people, and other items on board, *trim tanks* are used. The forward and after tanks are called simply forward trim and after trim. The two or three tanks amidships are known as auxiliary tanks. By varying the water (variable ballast) in these tanks a perfect *trim* can be attained and the submarine can hover in the sea, drifting in the current rather as a balloon drifts in the wind.

To help get the ship under water when it is in this weightless condition, a *negative tank* that adds the extra downward push may be carried. When the submarine gets well under, the water in the negative tank is blown overboard with compressed air.

Of course, in reality it never works out quite so smoothly. A last-minute change, or minor errors in the weight estimates for stores just received, means that the trim system must be used to shift variable ballast. The trim pump is started and the necessary water is pumped from forward trim to after trim or to where it is needed to correct the balance of the ship. Water can also be pumped overboard or flooded in.

To surface, the diving alarm is sounded three times and the word is passed, "Surface! Surface! Surface!" Compressed air, stored in several series of big bottles called *air banks,* is used to blow the water from the ballast tanks and, with positive buoyancy, the ship rises rapidly to the surface. At the surface the compressed air is turned off and a large "low pressure blower," an extremely powerful fan, forces more air into the tanks to expel the remaining water. In the meantime the air compressors are turned on at once to begin recharging the air banks. Air is precious on a submarine.

If a man is sealed up in a bank vault, his life may depend on how long the air holds out. The steel sides of a submerged submarine let in no more air than those of a bank vault. The submarine crews of yesterday had to worry about the supply of air on the ship.

Even during World War II, Allied submarines relied mainly upon the air that they took with them on diving. By using chemicals spread on mattress covers they could take some of the dangerous carbon dioxide

This complex ballast control panel keeps the submarine in perfect diving "trim."

(CO_2) that they exhaled out of the air, but this was an awkward emergency procedure. They could also add oxygen to the air to replace that which had been absorbed by breathing. The submarine carried enough oxygen to last the crew a day or so in case the ship met with disaster. This was enough, they hoped, to allow time for rescue.

We have seen how the Germans used the snorkel tube to let their submarine breathe while partially submerged. But the snorkel was still not good enough to enable the submarine to avoid detection by improved aircraft radar. When nuclear power was built into the *Nautilus*, her designers planned her so that neither the engines nor the crew required a source of air outside the ship itself.

The first problem, the oxygen supply for the crew, was handled with relative ease. Bottles of compressed oxygen were stored here and there in the ballast tanks. *Nautilus* carried enough oxygen for more than a month of total submergence.

The next step forward was the invention of chlorate candles, cylinders about the size of a medium fireplace log made of chemicals. Burned in a special furnace, they gave off oxygen. These worked perfectly, although they were bulky to store.

The latest oxygen-producing device is an *oxygen generator* that removes the oxygen from sea water by a special process. It moves even closer the day that a submarine can remain at sea for indefinite periods.

Next, the removal of the CO_2 being exhaled with every breath had to be engineered. A device called a CO_2 scrubber was designed and tested. The scrubber has a special chemical fluid that dissolves the CO_2 in the atmosphere. The loaded fluid is pumped into a chamber and stripped of CO_2 which is then pumped overboard. The CO_2 scrubber is no more trouble to run than a washing machine.

The carbon monoxide (CO) given off by cigarettes, cigars, or cooking is a deadly poison. It is the same gas that comes from automobile exhaust pipes and kills people in closed garages. Its effect is particularly bad since the victim can be totally unaware that he is being overcome. Yet the gas has one weakness that enables us to fight it. Since it is formed by incomplete combustion, it burns.

So it was easy to build burners to burn the CO and

other burnable gases in the air such as hydrogen. Hydrogen is given off when the electric storage battery is recharged after use in a drill or emergency. It is especially important to be rid of hydrogen because, when it is present in sufficient concentration, it explodes with the slightest spark.

The particles of smoke and bad odors that build up are handled in still another way. It is well known that carbon makes an excellent filter, and so a nuclear submarine contains carbon filters to remove impurities from the air.

The result of this *atmosphere control* is air as pure as one can breathe anywhere. Crew members suffering from hay fever are cured after a few hours submerged. There is no special smell at all.

Some precautions, however, need to be taken. The captain will issue strict orders against bringing on board anything that gives off a toxic gas. Certain liquid shoe polish, cleaning fluid, most mimeograph fluid, some glue for hobbies like building models, and a host of other items are forbidden because their use in a confined space would be dangerous.

Even painting the ship is subject to restrictions. An oil-base paint gives off unpleasant fumes until it is dry. The nose cannot detect it, but the paint goes on giving off fumes at a continually slower rate for weeks. So there is no painting at sea with oil-base paint. In port, painting has to be completed well before the next operation at sea, or water-base paint is used.

Sometimes, a shipyard worker will accidentally put paint on a steam line or other surface which gets

Here and there are banks of switches, which are vital to ship control submerged.

hot. The paint is then obscured with insulation material called lagging. As the pipe heats, it gives off pungent, burned paint smoke for a few days, bringing

tears to everyone's eyes and making things most unpleasant, though not dangerous.

Another urgent problem for a submarine is drinking
water. The nuclear submarine obtains water by the
same technique long used by diesel-electric submarines—but with novel results.

The principle is that of the *still*. Sea water is heated
in an evaporator tank at low pressure until the water
boils and evaporates. The salt is left behind and the
water vapor is then condensed into fresh water.

Diesel-electric submarines used electric evaporators
to provide fresh water, but they took precious electricity and had too low an output. Though there was
plenty of water for cooking and drinking, there was
little left over. The men could not take showers very
often, except for certain members of the crew who
handled food or who had particularly hot jobs in the
engine room. And there wasn't much water for
laundry.

On nuclear submarines all this is changed. Instead
of using electric power to heat the salt water, steam
from the reactor is used, and there is plenty of it.
Fresh water is needed for the reactor plant and for the
boilers; the designers, therefore, made sure that there
would be no shortage. Should the steam evaporator
fail, there is also an electric evaporator ready to take
over.

So now the crews have plenty of water. Showers can
be taken daily, and laundry done as needed. Wasting
water is discouraged, but there is definitely a cleaner
odor in a nuclear submarine.

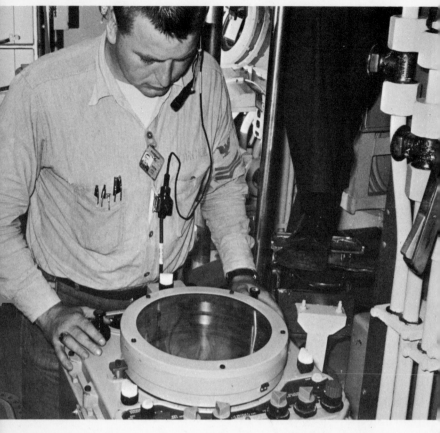

A crewman checks the position of the Polaris submarine, USS Patrick Henry, using the radar repeater scope.

The reactor's power is harnessed in another way. The heavy rudder and the diving planes on sail and stern have to be moved swiftly to maneuver the ship at high speed. This is done by hydraulic power.

Electric motors drive oil pumps which supply oil under pressure. When the helmsman or planesman turns the handwheel or moves the control column, pressurized oil forces an operating piston to move, causing movement of the control surfaces.

If the normal hydraulic system springs a leak or jams, then the emergency hydraulic system can be used. If that, too, fails, the man can move the control surfaces by pumping by hand—but this is exhausting, slow work.

The hydraulic system is used for such jobs as opening and shutting valves. The main vents that let air out of the ballast tanks when the submarine submerges are worked by this system. Hydraulic power raises and lowers the heavy masts used for radio communications and radar. It pushes up the periscope that allows the men below to see what is going on in the world above the sea surface.

The periscopes of the submarine are precision instruments with the magnification of a pair of powerful binoculars. Some navies have periscopes that permit the use of both eyes. The American instrument is not that comfortable, although it is a very sophisticated piece of equipment and can be looked through by either the right or left eye.

A typical periscope has a high and low magnification power adjustment, a means of focus, filters for various conditions of lighting, and a handle for raising the line of sight until the observer can look almost directly overhead. It can be used to measure the altitude of the sun or a star for navigation, or to get the range of an approaching ship by the split-image technique common to most cameras. Fine photographs can be taken through a periscope.

Some periscopes have a radar and even a radio antenna. No wonder the captain of a submarine is seen so often with his eye glued to the periscope, hugging it, the better to turn it around. A nuclear submarine captain prefers his ship to be deep and uses his periscope more sparingly than his predecessors in the diesel fleet.

In the depths a submarine can "see" with the sonars. Sonar was of great importance to submarines before the coming of nuclear power; today the nuclear submarine relies even more on sonar.

Of greatest use is the *passive,* or listening, sonar. It can hear a ship approaching long before the vessel can be seen through the periscope. The sonarman can often tell much about the stranger by the sounds it makes. Diesel engines, for example, make a different kind of noise from steam engines. A destroyer using *active* sonar, which throws out a sonar noise, or ping, in hopes of having it echo from a submarine, can be identified with ease.

The submarine can use active sonar, too. But since this gives away the position of the submarine, it is used only when passive sonar will not do the job. If an enemy submarine suddenly slows her engines and tries to sneak away, she may no longer be heard. Active sonar must then be used to keep her "in view."

The sonar room is small and crammed with complex electronic equipment. Every effort is made to make the room soundproof. The operators must be comfortable so that they can concentrate on their work. When a deep patrolling submarine hears a distant contact, the captain will often go to the sonar room to listen to it, just as he would climb to a bridge of a surface ship for a look.

If the assigned mission is to report the presence of any intruder, the nuclear submarine will raise an antenna mast and report by radio to base. To receive radio messages it is not even necessary to raise an antenna, so powerful are our Navy shore radio stations.

Voice radio can be used from a submarine direct to the Pentagon from any point on the high seas, including the Arctic ice pack. Conversations were held in 1960 between the USS *Seadragon* at the North Pole and the naval station at McMurdo Sound, Antarctica. The captain can just pick up the microphone on his raised platform at the periscope stand and talk to a passing airplane or ship, while watching it from below the surface.

The radio room often allows the crew to listen to commercial radio broadcasts that are being received. If everyone is busy, the late news will be put on tape so that the crew can hear it at mealtime.

Another problem the designers had to solve was that of waste disposal. In the old days a submarine would simply save up its garbage to toss overboard when it came to the surface. Weights were used to make the garbage sink out of sight in wartime so as to leave no trace for the enemy to find. Saving garbage during a sixty-day nuclear submarine patrol is just unthinkable.

The solution is the garbage ejector, a long tube

about ten inches in diameter extending from the galley straight down to the bottom of the ship. It has a door at top and bottom, with a connection at the top to both the salt-water flushing system and the compressed air system.

Garbage and trash are stowed in plastic bags. Tin cans are flattened and sharp edges are blunted before they are put in the bag. When enough accumulates,

Captain Edward L. Beach, commanding officer of the USS *Triton* (SSRN-586), informs the crew that the submarine is to circumnavigate the globe submerged.

the top door is opened and the bags are loaded until the garbage ejector is full. The top door is then closed and locked, the garbage ejector is flooded, and the bottom door is opened. A flow of salt water from the trim pump is used to flush the garbage clear. After an interval the outer door is closed, the tube is pumped dry, and the garbage ejector is ready for the next load.

Waste water and sewage are disposed of by a somewhat similar means. When a sanitary tank is full, the various drains leading to it are closed off. The discharge valve to sea is opened, the tank is blown almost dry with compressed air, the discharge valve is closed, and the air pressure in the tank is slowly vented back into the ship through deodorizing charcoal filters.

Almost everything about the ship is complex. But it is complexity with a purpose. And as the crew members live with it, it becomes no more bewildering than a kitchen at home.

5

UNDERWATER WEAPONS

THE SUBMARINE is primarily a weapon of war. It exists to attack. No roar of guns proclaim its fighting. A barely audible sigh as the hydraulic torpedo tube doors swing open is all an enemy submarine has a chance to hear, a noise that is usually lost in the slap of waves and the clamor of busy fish.

A homing torpedo, swimming quietly toward the target, resembles its submarine mother. Listening and then aiming itself relentlessly at the enemy, it soon rams its explosive head into the foe's hull.

The cigar-shaped torpedo is not a new weapon. It was perfected in 1867 by a Scot, Robert Whitehead, working from an idea provided by an Austrian naval officer named Lupis. But it was a puny weapon by to-day's standards. Powered by compressed air, the Whitehead torpedo would not go above 8 knots; its range was a scant 400 yards. The next seventy-five years produced slow but steady changes.

In World War II Japan used a hydrogen-peroxide torpedo called the "long lance," the most remarkable torpedo of the war. It would do 49 knots for a distance of more than 12 land miles.

The United States Navy has developed a modern version of this kind of "fish." It is approximately 20 feet long, 21 inches in diameter, and weighs about 4,000 pounds. In the nose is a detonator and a powerful explosive charge.

This torpedo is driven by two propellers rotated in opposite directions by a turbine. The turbine is similar to the one in a nuclear submarine; it is turned by steam and gas formed by spraying water into burning hydrogen peroxide and alcohol.

Control surfaces at the tail keep the torpedo on the preset course and at the proper depth. A gyro in the tail steers the torpedo while a combination pendulum and depth-sensing switch maintains it at the preset running depth. Most United States submarines can carry more than two dozen of these torpedoes on an antishipping mission.

The aiming, or *fire control,* of such weapons is not easy although it is not complicated in theory. The simplest of shots is the straight running torpedo aimed at a surface ship. Suppose an enemy ship's mast has just been sighted. The rest of her, superstructure and hull, is out of sight over the horizon. She is coming our way.

"Battle stations torpedo!" cries the public address system. Officers and men dash to their stations. The officer of the deck shows the captain the prey through the periscope.

"Left full rudder!" orders the captain, turning his ship to an intercepting course. A funnel tilted aft and a kingpost appear. She is a large freighter alone. As

A torpedoman checks the torpedo tubes. Notice the noses of the four torpedoes which are ready to be loaded.

the captain describes the ship to his fire control party, it looks like an easy kill.

A football passer cocking his arm to throw has much the same problem as the submarine fire control party. It does no good to aim directly at the pass receiver. So the halfback asks himself, "By how much do I lead the end running across the field?" Then he throws to the place where he expects the end to be by the time the football arrives.

The solution to the fire control problem lies in the direction the torpedo should be shot so that it will arrive at a point in the ocean at the same time as the target. The course the torpedo steers is figured out by a combination of the plot and instruments. The plot is a large sheet of paper on which the enemy ship's position and the submarine's position are drawn to scale. Then the enemy's course and speed are figured out graphically (the halfback does this in his head) and the direction to the point of intercept of torpedo and enemy ship can be computed.

Meanwhile the electromechanical and electronic instruments are silently computing. The target is going to the right at 17 knots and will be there when the torpedo crosses its path. Therefore, the torpedo should steer southwest to hit.

The twelve officers and men who comprise the fire control party and work these plots and instruments also figure out the spread angles between torpedoes. The steel fish must fan out so that they act like the pellets of a shotgun shell as they search for a bird on the wing. Up to six torpedoes may be in a fan probing for a target.

The executive officer, the second in command, is the fire control coordinator, a misleading title meaning that he is the head of the fire control party. When he is satisfied that the fire control party has a good solu-

A torpedo is loaded aboard the USS *Patrick Henry*. Polaris submarines carry torpedoes as well as Polaris missiles.

tion for the direction in which to shoot torpedoes, he recommends opening fire.

The captain, agreeing, will order—"Final bearing and shoot!" The periscope goes up for one last check on the location of the target; a last-minute change in course by the target must not be missed. The firing key is pressed. A shudder runs through the ship as the first torpedo is forced from the torpedo tube by a terrific jet of water. One after another, the torpedoes dash away, jarring the submarine slightly. In less than a minute white, towering plumes of water rise from the explosions, nearly obscuring the enemy ship.

A single hit by a torpedo will blow a hole in a merchant ship the size of a garage entrance. To increase torpedo damage a magnetic exploder may be used. Around the large mass of iron of a ship's hull is a magnetic field. When a torpedo enters this field, its magnetic exploder triggers, detonating the warhead.

Large modern surface warships are built to survive several torpedo hits. It takes more than one torpedo, usually, to sink a destroyer. A great modern aircraft carrier could doubtless shake off six or more torpedoes tipped with conventional explosives, although in World War II one huge Japanese carrier was sunk by a single torpedo because of her faulty design and incredibly bad damage control measures by an inexperienced crew. A surface warship has a number of compartments that can be isolated in order to contain an inrush of water. A submerged submarine is, of course, more vulnerable in case of a direct hit, but it has a good chance of surviving a near miss because its rugged construction enables it to go to great depths.

Merchant captains have long used tricks that helped them to avoid being hit by a spread of torpedoes, if they were detected in time. As soon as the white wakes of the old steam torpedoes were spotted, the wheel was put over and the ship was turned toward them in an effort to steer her between the wakes. Sometimes this was successful and torpedoes passed harmlessly down either side of the vessel.

Once in a while a ship with good backing power can reverse its engines and slow down enough for the torpedo to go harmlessly ahead. Speeding up is rarely of any use to a lumbering merchantman.

Torpedo wakes are almost invisible at night except in tropic seas where phosphorescence causes illuminated trails to appear behind the speeding fish. German torpedo designers of World War II tried to get rid of the telltale daytime wakes.

The use of electric storage batteries for propulsion eliminated the wakes caused by exhaust gas and smoke from the burning alcohol and oil of older torpedoes. Hydrogen-peroxide torpedoes are also essentially wakeless, and they are now favored because they can go faster than electric torpedoes.

Even more difficult to avoid than the straight-running torpedo is a pattern-running torpedo. A pattern runner zigzags about on courses designed to bring it back on target even if it misses the enemy ship on the first trip. But a ship could still escape the pattern-running torpedo if the fire control solution has been faulty and the torpedo is sent off course. Why not build an "intelligent" torpedo that could head for a noisy ship in the same way as the submarine itself, that is, by means of sonar?

The German designers fashioned an electric torpedo considerably shorter and lighter than the hydrogen-peroxide type. Instead of steering a preset course to the end of its run, this torpedo goes out to a predetermined point and begins a sonar search. The noise of the target is sensed by hydrophones in the nose of the torpedo. Electronic circuits convert these signals into orders to the torpedo's steering rudders.

The performance tests given to early versions of these torpedoes earned them the name "cuties." When the torpedoman scratched his fingers along the left side of the nose of one of these cuties as it lay in the reload position in the torpedo room, the torpedo rudder slapped to the left to try to follow the noise that the "left" hydrophone was detecting. Scratching the nose on the upper portion caused the torpedo's planes to snap into the "up" position as if the fish were alive.

Surface ships soon learned to tow noise-making devices behind them, which often effectively decoyed homing torpedoes which would sometimes leap clear out of the water in excitement over the decoy. Unable to find anything solid to hit and running out of electricity, the torpedo would slow to a stop and sink harmlessly to the bottom.

United States submarines at sea today have as their primary target, not surface ships, but *other submarines*. Hunting that kind of wary game requires more sophisticated weapons.

The latest homing torpedo is most complicated. It has so many new features that veteran submariners needed to have special target practice to learn to use it when it first appeared. When the enemy is in *sight*, the alerted torpedo wiggles its tail, speeds up, changes depth, and rams into the enemy. It doesn't have to carry as much explosive as the antimerchantman torpedo. A hole the size of a basketball will do the job and put an enemy submarine out of commission. Still newer and far more powerful weapons exist.

The submarine can also use another weapon of war

against its own kind—the mine. Mines laid by submarines have aided the torpedo in the destruction of enemy shipping. Special mine-laying submarines were used in World War I and World War II. Racks of mines were fitted to the hulls of some mine-layers (now mine-laying is done by submarines using the torpedo tubes, and it is not necessary to build special submarines for the purpose).

In the beginning submarine mines were simple like those laid by surface ships and airplanes. A package was ejected from the submarine to drop to the bottom. After a short interval the explosive-laden chamber detached itself from the anchor and rose to a position just below the surface of the water.

A submarine could lay several dozen of these deadly devices and a surface ship striking a mine received even greater damage than from a single torpedo hit.

As minesweepers learned to deal with these mines— by cutting their anchor cables and sinking or exploding them by rifle fire when they floated to the surface —the mine designers became more devious. Mines were designed that made use of methods other than contact for triggering the explosive.

The magnetic principle used in the torpedo exploder was employed in the mine. In defense, ships began to loop great coils of wire about their hulls. When a powerful current of electricity was passed through these degaussing coils, the magnetic field about the ship was neutralized and magnetic mines did not detect that a ship had passed.

Today the most devilish mines are the pressure

mines, lying on the bottom with ship counters in them. Near most ports there is shallow water. When a ship passes into the shallow water, its bottom is close enough to the ground to cause a pressure wave. The mine, feeling the pressure, explodes. Of course, there would be a determined effort by the other side to eliminate the mine field, and that is where the counter comes into use.

The submarine crew sets the counter so that the mines are not exploded by the first ship to go over the field. When set this way a mine counts up to, say, four ships passing by and then goes off under the fifth. In this way the enemy is kept off balance. He cannot be sure if a new mine field has been laid and must go into the minesweeping routine while the port stops all business.

Submarines can use mines to force shipping away from a coast. Running a convoy of ships in close to the beach is a clever tactic because between the beach and the ships the submarine does not have enough water in which to operate. All attention and protection can be directed seaward. But if mines are laid across this path, the ships in the convoy have to turn to deeper water to get by safely and thus become easier targets for submarine attack.

In some areas the submarine uses the torpedo mine. These mobile mines may run along for several miles into a harbor or river mouth. Once in its predetermined position the propelled mine sinks to await its prey.

However, conventional explosives in submarine

weapons are giving way more and more to nuclear warheads of awesome destructiveness. And, increasingly, the submarine has turned to the missile to add speed and range to its offensive punch.

6

THERMONUCLEAR MISSILES
SUBMERGE

TORPEDOES are accurate and deadly underwater missiles. They have been used as weapons by submarines for many years.

Torpedoes are short-range missiles and can be fired only at targets that are within sight or easy sonar range of the submarine. Modern naval warfare requires long-range missiles that can hit a target that may be hundreds or thousands of miles away from the launching ship. Long-range missiles could be mounted on surface ships, but the surface ship can be found and followed by enemy submarines, surface ships, and aircraft. The submarine, on the other hand, is an invisible launching site, and can bring the target within firing range.

In the early 1950s United States Navy scientists and technicians developed Regulus, an air-breathing missile that could be carried by a submarine. Regulus was launched successfully from the diesel-electric submarine *Tunny* on July 15, 1953. The nonpiloted craft had a range of 500 miles, and flew at an altitude of about 30,000 feet at about 600 miles per hour. It could be fitted with a nuclear warhead far more powerful than the atomic bomb which destroyed Hiroshima, Japan, in 1945.

The Regulus was designed to be carried in a submarine hangar that could be opened up rapidly when the ship surfaced. The bird was then brought out and readied for firing. In a few minutes it was being guided toward the target by powerful radar commands from the launching submarine. The command could even be taken over by another submarine at periscope depth, and closer to the target, to give final guidance for the plunge into the objective.

Regulus was highly successful, and an improved version, Regulus II, with a thousand-mile range and a speed of 1,600 miles per hour, was designed and tested. A nuclear submarine, the *Halibut*, was completed in 1960 with an especially large hangar to hold a number of Regulus missiles. It was expected that a series of such ships would be built.

But technology was moving rapidly. And as early as November 1955, the Navy stated its intention to develop a ballistic missile that could be fired from a totally submerged submarine. A ballistic missile differs from a nonpiloted craft such as Regulus in that it can soar to a target without the guidance of radar or any other external guidance system. Another advantage of the ballistic missile is its great speed. It is much faster than the fastest jet aircraft, which is essentially what Regulus is. A ballistic missile can also be prepared for firing much more rapidly than a Regulus-type missile.

In January 1958, the first fleet ballistic missile

(FBM) test flight was made at Point Mugu, California. The new missile was called Polaris, after the North Star that has been a guide to seamen through the ages.

By the time *Halibut* was ready to go to sea with her Regulus missile, the *George Washington* was also in the water and preparing for action. On July 20, 1960, the *George Washington* successfully fired a Polaris test vehicle while submerged off Cape Canaveral, Florida. Naval warfare had reached a turning point.

While there remained much to do to perfect the Polaris system, there was no point in extending the Regulus program. And although it had been a complete success, it was halted.

A Polaris is not huge as missiles go, but at 15 tons it

The nuclear-powered USS *Halibut* (SSGN-587) surfaces to shoot her Regulus-I guided missiles.

is not small either. About 28 feet long, it is approximately four and a half feet in diameter.

The Polaris, or FBM, is propelled by solid fuel designed to push it 1,380 land miles. A new version of the Polaris (the A-2) is two and a half feet longer and goes 1,725 land miles. Still another improved version (the A-3) will go more than 2,500 land miles.

A system for firing missiles from the sea has certain advantages over one that is land-based. For example, an aggressor would know the general location of the major missile launching sites in the United States, but he could not know from what direction to expect a Polaris attack. His antimissile defense system, therefore, must be large, facing in all directions, and enormously complicated. (As a protection against ballistic missiles, antimissile missiles—missiles that can intercept and destroy other missiles while in flight—are being developed.) Because a submarine can launch a Polaris attack from waters near enemy territory, Polaris missiles do not have to travel as far as land-based missiles, thereby giving the enemy less time to get his antimissile missiles in the air to shoot them down. So far no country has built a defense system that can protect it from such a sea-based attack.

When the USS *Ethan Allen* successfully fired a Polaris missile during the nuclear-weapon test series in May 1962, one observer said that the nuclear blast went off "right in the pickle barrel." There can no longer be any doubt about the deadly effectiveness of the United States nuclear submarine armed with ballistic missiles.

In time of war, Polaris missiles would probably be the first American weapons on target, since they can be brought closer to enemy territory than the intercontinental missiles launched from the United States. They can also beat liquid-fueled intermediate-range missiles from overseas bases because this type of missile requires longer preparation.

An aggressor would have an insuperable task trying to shoot down the hundreds of missiles raining from the different directions in which Polaris submarines can be hidden in the ocean. Plan as he might to destroy our missile bases abroad and at home, he could not know, even by the best spy work, the exact location at sea, at any given instant, of our Polaris submarines.

Launched under the water by compressed air from the submarine's great vertical missile tubes, the Polaris bounds to the surface and is away in a roar and spectacular belch of white smoke. The engines exert thrust through four nozzles in the base of the rocket. After launch and after the fuel is exhausted, the first stage drops away and the second stage rocket engines take over the final acceleration.

Small blast deflectors called jetevators are used to steer the missile so that it stays on its predetermined flight path. The guidance system is built in the missile itself, and it is accurate enough to compare favorably with that of any other ballistic missile in its ability to pinpoint targets at maximum range.

Here is how the Polaris works. The exact position of the ship that is launching the Polaris must be known at all times. The position of the Polaris submarine to-

A Polaris ballistic missile soars toward the target from a submarine submerged off Cape Canaveral. Unlike the guided missile Regulus, Polaris, once fired, needs no radar guidance.

gether with the position of the target determines the flight path. The target remains stationary, but the submarine does not.

There are a number of methods by which an FBM submarine can obtain exact position computations. One of these is the ship's inertial navigation system (SINS). SINS is a new system. It consists of a complicated arrangement of gyros and accelerometers (devices that sense movement of the ship over the ground) together with computing circuits that indicate the ship's position at all times. To be absolutely safe the Polaris submarine has three SINS that check on each other, but their errors are amazingly small.

Electronically through the SINS, by using the periscope at infrequent intervals for observation of the stars, and by other secret means, the Polaris submarine fixes its position with the required exactness. The position is fed continuously into the fire control system.

From the fire control system electronic circuits carry the necessary information to the missile itself: where the target is, where the ship is, what direction is north, and even which way is up! The flight path or trajectory is also furnished.

Missile guidance is tricky, but that of the Polaris missile is well designed and proved.

The missile carries an electronic computer and the gyroscopes and accelerometers of an inertial navigation system. At firing, this guidance package puts the missile on the proper course to hit the target. What happens if it is launched into a hurricane?

The furious winds and waves of a big storm will

throw the missile off course, as could other things such as increased speed from the launching submarine at the time of firing. In such an event the guidance system computes a new course to the target and steers the missile onto it with the jetevators. The guidance system keeps the missile stable, preventing rolling or any form of unusual motion. It also has another vital function.

The target will rarely lie at the extreme range of the missile. This means that before all the fuel in the second stage is burned, the rocket motors must be cut off at the correct instant or the missile will overshoot the target. The guidance package stops the rocket motor and then causes the separation of the second stage from the capsule containing the nuclear bomb. This capsule is called the reentry body because it must reenter the earth's atmosphere. From this point on, the nuclear warhead needs no guidance and plunges down into its burst point at the target.

The burst of the Polaris warhead has hideous force. For example, it could smash a great city like New York, not only causing death and destruction on Manhattan Island but spreading damage and injury much beyond that area. A Polaris submarine carries sixteen of these terrible weapons ready for action at all times.

Polaris and Regulus are not the only nuclear-tipped missiles that can be fired by United States submarines. Subroc is a new addition to the arsenal of weapons. Subroc is designed to kill an enemy submarine, although it could be used to attack surface ships or shore installations. It may be carried by both antisubmarine submarines and Polaris submarines. Subroc is important because its range is many times that of a torpedo, and because it gets to the target so *fast*.

When the target is located, a Subroc is fired from a torpedo tube. It rises swiftly to the surface and emerges with rocket engines screaming to streak across the sky heading for the enemy. A missile can go much faster in thin air than a torpedo can in water. It is similar to the difference in speed between a jet aircraft and an automobile. With Subroc there is little time for an enemy submarine to move far away, even if she knows that she is under attack.

When Subroc reaches the target, the warhead enters the water and sinks quickly to a predetermined depth where the nuclear blast is triggered. Any enemy submarine within thousands of yards would be killed or sorely wounded by the titanic explosion. Even the firing submarine, miles away, would be shaken like a dog by the blast.

The submarine with Subroc has the tremendous advantage, well known to prize fighters, of longer reach over its torpedo-firing predecessors. The day is gone when it is necessary to get practically close enough to ram the enemy in order to launch weapons successfully.

The United States is not the only naval power with submarine-launched missiles. The Soviet Union has them also. Soviet missiles are often mounted in vertical tubes like those of the United States, but theirs are concentrated in the sail and are fewer in number. The first such Soviet missile submarines were diesel-electric, but later Soviet versions are believed to be nuclear-powered and may mount more missiles.

The United States now has a definite advantage over the Soviet Union in the number and quality of submarine-launched missiles on station at sea. This advantage can be maintained, but it will take the hardest kind of work.

Part of this superiority, a very large part, depends upon the excellence of the crews of both antisubmarine and Polaris nuclear submarines. To understand how highly complex weapons can be kept ready to use and fired accurately from on board a submarine submerged many feet, we must meet the men of the submarine service.

7
THE MAKING OF A
NUCLEAR SUBMARINE CREW

SAILORS on nuclear submarines have at least two things in common. They are intelligent and they want to serve in submarines. In other respects they represent a broad cross-section of the population of the United States. Clipped Maine speech, southern accents, and western drawls may be heard on board almost any submarine.

Recruiting stations all over the country are busy every working day sizing up new candidates for the Navy's nuclear submarines. The final decision as to whether a man steps aboard a submarine depends on his performance during extensive training and exhaustive tests. However, the Navy recruiter is usually quite accurate in judging which recruits will be able to make the grade and join the submarine service. Suppose a high school senior asks him, "Can I be a nuclear submariner?"

Submariners are surrounded by highly complex mechanical, electrical, and electronic equipment. They must know how to operate and repair it. A submarine man has to be of above-average intelligence. A careful scrutiny of the candidate's grades in high school is part of the routine check to see if he is submarine material.

Willingness to work is another important qualification. And a senior's school record will certainly show this. Did he steadily improve his grades; or once a respectable grade was obtained did he sit back and relax? Does he have a part time job? Are his interests of a frothy or silly nature, or is he seriously preparing himself for life?

Since submariners live in close quarters for weeks and months at a time, there is no room for the man with annoying habits or a grating personality. A young man with a sunny disposition, whose record shows he enjoys mixing with others in extracurricular activities and sports, is preferred.

Discipline on board a submarine is informal and the individual who has to be watched in order to get him to do the right thing is most unwelcome. There is a minimum of standing at attention at muster. The men are expected to be at their stations and to do their work without prodding or detailed supervision.

Ashore there will be endless opportunities for the emotionally immature sailor to get into trouble. When a submarine crew member is involved with the authorities, the uniform and the entire ship are disgraced.

In order to keep those with little self-discipline out of submarines, an investigation is made of the recruit's behavior in his home town and school. What was thought a childish prank at the time may now loom large. Is it disqualifying evidence of instability?

Luckily, the United States has great numbers of

smart, technically minded young men with no emotional problems, who love adventure. They enlist daily and are sent to basic recruit training.

At the completion of this six-week period, the new sailor may go directly to submarine training. But more likely, he will go first to the school which starts him on the road to being a skilled technician. The machinist's mate, electronic technician, electrician, interior communication electrician's mate, fire control technician, and other specialists do work that is too complicated to learn on the job. Every enlisted man on the submarine must have or learn some specialty.

There are men who do not choose submarines on completion of recruit training but who later ask for duty in submarines. They leave their ships and stations to attend submarine school with candidates direct from recruit training and from the technical schools, at the famous submarine base in New London, Connecticut.

The principles of operating a submarine are drummed into them by experienced senior petty officers. They go to sea in training submarines to get a firsthand knowledge of how all the fluid, mechanical, electrical, and electronic systems fit together. At every step of the course there are quizzes and marks; and the class honor man wins a gold wristwatch.

One test is physical rather than mental. The submarine service is proud of its safety record. But one can never tell when disaster may strike. If a submarine should be helpless on the sea bottom, the crew must know how to escape to the surface.

So the students are taken to the escape training tank. This tank is more than 100 feet high and 18 feet in diameter. It is filled with fresh water. Into its sides, at three levels, are built locks through which men may enter the column of water to practice making escapes at different depths.

First, thorough instruction in escape techniques is given the student, and the candidates are examined

The escape training tank at the submarine base in New London, Connecticut, is more than 100 feet high.

to be sure that they are fit. Then comes the pressure test.

A dozen students and an instructor climb into a round steel drum the size of a trailer-truck van. Behind them a thick steel door closes with a solid clank.

As the students sit apprehensively on benches along each side of the tank, a hiss of air signals the mounting pressure. Swallowing to equalize the pressure of their eardrums, the men watch the pressure gauge mount toward 50 pounds per square inch. If anyone has difficulty adjusting, perhaps because a cold has plugged his ear or because of a poor filling in a tooth, the instructor at once reduces the pressure to zero and lets the unlucky man out to try again another day.

Those who pass this pressure test move to the elevator to go to the top of the tank. Around the tank is a wide walkway with safety apparatus mounted here and there. Since the tank is covered, it resembles a circular indoor swimming pool. Standing at the water's edge the students watch instructors demonstrate the use of the Steinke hood in the free buoyant ascent method of escape. The hood is pulled completely over the head, and all the man has to do is to leave the lock and float to the surface, making sure that he breathes normally as he rises. Now it is the students' turn.

Down they go in the elevator to enter the shallow lock, only 18 feet deep. Eight men at a time crowd into the gray metal steel chamber not much bigger than a bathroom. Their ears are filled with the roar of water spouting in through a big pipe. They watch the water rise over their feet. Each man must swallow rapidly to relieve the pressure in his ears. Any tendency toward claustrophobia is stamped out here. After this nothing will ever feel quite so cramped and close.

When the water is at nose level the pressure is equalized and the door to the tank is opened. Giving a final adjustment to the Steinke hood, each man steps out of the door into the comfortably heated water of the escape tank to float rapidly to the surface.

After eight weeks of intensive training the submarine school class goes to operating submarines. The new men now make their reputation among the friendly yet critical members of a submarine's crew.

Their next goal is submarine qualification and the silver twin dolphin insignia of the submarine service. In a seven-month period a submariner is expected to learn all the intricacies of the ship, demonstrate ability to operate equipment, and know how to be a real help in emergencies. Of course this is not his only assignment.

A submarine crew is divided into departments. Some departments are large enough to have divisions. There are the Operations, Engineering, Supply, Navigation, Medical, and Weapons departments. A new man is assigned to one of these departments and must help with the routine cleaning and repair work as well as stand watches.

The way that the departments are organized gives a clue to another important training subject for the crew: leadership. In each department or division there will be a seasoned chief, or first-class petty officer, who will be the "leading" petty officer. It is his job to see

Lieutenant Harris Steinke, USN (right), developed this mummy-like hood, a new escape appliance which is effective at depths as great as 400 feet.

that his men are organized to perform the assigned work, and that they do it quickly and efficiently.

A leading petty officer will maintain the standard of dress and cleanliness. He will pass on requests for leave or extra liberty. He goes before the captain when one of his men is reported for an offense and offers his evaluation of the man's character and work. He is called upon to perform the tasks requiring the most skill in his specialty, and he must teach his men all the tricks of the trade.

The lower-rated men are further subdivided in their responsibilities for specific items of equipment or routine work. They may have assistants working for them.

One man is detailed as the "water king." He is responsible for keeping account of fresh water on board. Another is responsible for keeping engineering logs and records, and yet another is charged with keeping the spare parts straight.

The watch organization is most important, too. Each man is trained to stand a watch. It may be as a helmsman, or auxiliary electrician, or perhaps in the lower-level engine room. At sea some watch is assigned to almost every enlisted man on board.

A new junior man may well end up with a two-month tour as "mess cook" in the supply department. The mess cook is charged with assisting the cook in setting up for meals and in cleaning up. A man can find no better way to earn the respect of his new shipmates than to handle this lowly assignment cheerfully and efficiently. They, after all, have done this themselves and know how difficult and prosaic it is.

At the submarine school realistic training devices are used to teach sailor students how to control a submerged submarine.

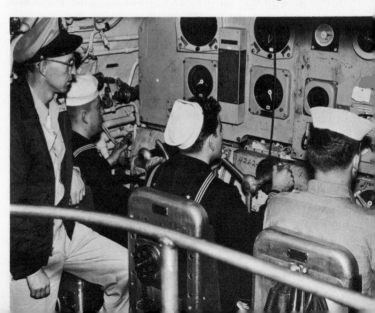

The individual specialties to which he will be assigned after qualification are anything but prosaic. He may work on the great Polaris missiles or control the terrific forces locked inside the nuclear reactor. He may assist in navigating the ship or receive and decipher (decode) radio messages. He may become responsible for operation and repair of the complex radar or help make sonar work as the eyes and ears of the submerged submarine.

What he does is up to him, but he must choose. In some cases the requirements may narrow an individual's choice. For example, not everyone has the background or aptitude for nuclear-power training.

If he has not had special training before reporting to a submarine the newly qualified submariner is usually sent to school to enhance his value to the ship. These school courses vary in length, depending upon the subject matter. Some of the longest ones are those in fire control (24 weeks), radio (24 weeks), electronics (28 weeks), and nuclear power, which is a full year.

Nuclear-power training probably represents the hardest course of instruction. It is given only to those who will serve as machinist's mates, enginemen, electronic technicians, electrician's mates, or interior-communication electrician's mates; for these are the men who run the nuclear-propulsion plant.

An identical six months theoretical course is given at the two nuclear-power schools at Bainbridge, Maryland, and Mare Island, California. This course covers mathematics, college algebra and calculus, chemistry, physics, metallurgy, reactor principles, reactor technology, thermodynamics, and related subjects. Examination follows examination. A slide rule is a constant companion of the nuclear-power trainee.

Next the man goes to a nuclear-power training unit at Windsor, Connecticut; West Milton, New York; or Arco, Idaho. Here are submarine nuclear-propulsion plants installed ashore. Although the reactors are operated primarily for making tests for the Atomic Energy Commission, sufficient time is allowed in conjunction with these tests for the Navy trainees to learn to operate the plants.

First they study the physical layout. Every pipe is traced out with its valves and components. Every electric circuit breaker is found and studied so that its purpose and the source of its closing power are known. The men must learn to operate everything. A tremendous amount of data must be committed to memory: tank capacities, rated output of generators and pumps, limits of operations in terms of temperature and pressure, and the like.

At every step, an instructor must be satisfied that the student actually knows that part of the plant, and he certifies it by initialing the student's record. At the end, the successful sailor is qualified as a reactor operator, and is sent to duty in the engineering department of a nuclear submarine.

Many men double in specialty jobs on nuclear submarines. There are special courses for skindivers who go over the side to inspect or repair hull fittings. There are men trained in stainless-steel welding, silver braz-

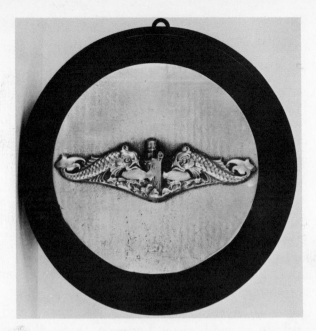

Qualification aboard a submarine entitles a man to wear the dolphin insignia—silver for enlisted men, gold for officers.

ing, and water chemistry—these last check the purity of the water used in the nuclear reactor and boilers.

The Navy also provides special schooling on how to operate such complex items as air conditioning, oxygen generators, inertial navigation systems, periscopes, hydraulics, torpedoes, and even motion-picture projectors.

With all of this intensive individual training and the resulting special skills, one might think that the submarine crews would be trained almost to a fault. But this is only the beginning.

Just as individual stars need training to function as a football team, so a crew needs practice together to make the ship effective. Team-training is carried out on board and ashore.

Aboard ship, drills of all kinds are conducted on a regular basis. The men work out battle problems culminating in the shooting of torpedoes. There are emergency drills such as fire, collision, and steam leak, and practice in rapidly shutting down the reactor. Man-overboard drills and bringing the ship alongside a pier are team efforts and require practice.

In port the fire control party can work inside mock attack-trainers whose periscopes look out at model ships that are maneuvered electrically over a game floor. Sonar operators attend training sessions, and communication drills are run.

Just to be sure that nothing has been missed and to provide a comparison between ships, the squadron commander gives an operational-readiness inspection to the ships in the squadron every year. A squadron normally consists of about ten submarines organized in two divisions of five submarines each, with a submarine tender and rescue vessel. The inspecting party comes aboard for a period of two days and observes and grades the ship's company on shooting weapons and conducting drills of every description.

Once a year submarines are selected to do an escape exercise with rescue vessels. Lying on the ocean bottom the submarine waits as the rescue vessel moors overhead and sends down a diving bell to rest on the submarine's escape hatch. Members of the submarine crew actually enter the bell and are hauled to the surface.

Just how well the crews learn to do their jobs individually and as a team is soon apparent when they are put to a real test. When an actual fire breaks out the crew leaps into furious action, shutting down equipment, setting boundaries to the flame and smoke, donning breathing apparatus, rescuing stricken comrades, and fighting the fire with fire extinguishers or hoses with fog nozzles fitted to spray water vapor on the fire. Emergency ventilation is started, alternate equipment is put into operation, and soon all is under control. Then repairs can begin. Anyone who has seen these magnificent crews in action can testify to the excellence of the Navy's training.

Directing the crew in its training, setting the standards, and furnishing the command leadership are the commissioned officers. The way they are chosen and trained is vital to the performance of the ship.

8

SUBMARINE OFFICERS

FROM THE START of his career, the goal of the young nuclear-trained submarine officer is command of his own submarine. Other duties on board can be most rewarding, but it is the thought of being an independent captain and executing an important mission that beckons.

If the nuclear submarine officer does a good job there is every hope that he will achieve his desire, because most of the high hurdles lie behind him. Many who began the journey toward submarine command with him have been dropped out. It is not easy to become a naval officer or to qualify in nuclear power and become a submariner.

It all starts in high school. High grades are important, but the kind of subjects studied are significant, too. Mathematics (all one can get), physics, chemistry, and other science courses are the basis for understanding modern technology. Courses in English and literature are also useful because the submarine officer writes many reports and official papers.

Only boys with good high school grades can go on to college and join the NROTC, or attend the United

States Naval Academy. The subjects studied in college have a major influence on a later naval career. The student who chooses business administration or art as a major cannot hope to enter submarines.

In Washington the Bureau of Naval Personnel and the Atomic Energy Commission each year evaluate senior class midshipmen through the country. Surprising as it might seem to bright NROTC students of the University of Oklahoma, for example, a board of officers at the Capital is familiar with their academic standing and general aptitude.

There are never enough top-quality candidates for nuclear-power training. It is not that too few apply, but the board will take only those who are qualified. Often places at the nuclear-power schools have gone empty because the Navy and the AEC refuse to lower the standards.

The members of the board study the men's performance records hoping to find candidates who will justify the expense of bringing them to Washington for an interview. Vice Admiral Hyman G. Rickover, the stern boss of the Navy and AEC nuclear reactor program, personally passes on each applicant.

The selection of Naval Academy and NROTC midshipmen for direct entry in nuclear-power training generally occurs in February and March. The candidates arrive in Washington and go to a dingy old two-story building off Constitution Avenue, where Admiral Rickover maintains his headquarters.

The midshipmen's first impression is usually one of wonder that such a renowned organization could work in such shabby, unpretentious surroundings. But Admiral Rickover disdains the trappings of power and refuses to spend the taxpayers' money for the usual rugs and overstuffed furniture. It may be the first, but it is certainly not the last evidence to the candidate that this organization is *different*.

Early one evening Admiral Rickover was in his office discussing an important reactor safety problem with the author of this book when a sudden rustling was heard. Where the radiator piping crossed the wall behind the Admiral's chair a large rat walked cautiously along. It peered suspiciously at me and then scurried on its way into the next office through the pipe opening in the wall.

Student officers are trained to handle emergencies. Here the *Nautilus* makes an emergency surface near a destroyer.

"What's the matter?" asked the Admiral, mildly annoyed at my sudden, obvious lapse of attention.

"A rat just ran across the room behind you, sir," I replied quickly, recovering from my surprise.

"So what? We have lots of rats in Washington," he snorted. "I'm used to them!"

Better security is maintained for human beings. The young visitor enters the headquarters through guarded doors and must identify himself. He is then conducted to a conference room to await his turn for an interview.

A preliminary interview is given individually by each of three officers on Admiral Rickover's staff. They want to know all about the candidate's record in school, his interests, and his seriousness of purpose. Does he *want* to work?

Next the Admiral himself probes into the midshipman's qualifications. He does not want anyone whom he has not personally examined to run a naval nuclear reactor. Admiral Rickover's interviews can be grueling experiences.

After graduation and upon receiving the officer's commission, the successful midshipman reports to one of the same two nuclear-power schools that teach the enlisted men. But he does not take the same courses of instruction during his six months of training.

The officer's nuclear-power course is an "advanced" course. The instructors do their best to make it live up to that description as they teach classes in mathematics, advanced physics, thermodynamics, chemistry, metallurgy, reactor plant engineering, electronics, reactor and power plant control, and servomechanisms. It is not an easy school, but the student officers are so well screened that few fail to complete it satisfactorily.

The officers next go to nuclear reactor prototypes for operational training. They must learn everything that the enlisted men do, and more. After the officer completes the enlisted reactor-operator qualification he moves on to qualify as engineering officer of the watch (EOOW). The EOOW is the person who is on watch in charge of the entire nuclear propulsion plant and of the men running it. Aboard ship he is also called the engineering officer of the watch.

It is essential that the engineering officer of the watch has a thorough grasp of the inner workings of the various parts of the propulsion plant. He must be able to react instantly and properly to trouble. A fast pace is required; the six months at the prototype is little enough time to learn so much.

Next comes submarine school at New London, Connecticut. The objective of this school is to teach the young officer enough about each of the departments aboard ship, such as weapons or supply, that he will be immediately useful upon going aboard. He may have to take over one of these departments at once.

Student officers are taught details of submarine construction, how to dive and surface a submarine, and how to maneuver the ship underneath the surface of the sea or alongside a pier.

The school has a number of diving trainers. These are full scale replicas of a submarine's diving station. As the student officers dive the ship, it tilts down under their feet and the depth gauge shows the ship descending. They can maneuver using the diving planes, blow main ballast to surface, and carry out realistic casualty drills.

Since the new submarine officer will be a member of the ship's fire control party, he must be taught the principles of approach and attack. He spends many hours in the school's attack-teacher, where actual equipment can be used. In order to understand how best to help their captain, the student officers rotate through the job of captain during these periods.

The best part of the submarine school course is the time spent underway in a submarine. The students have several overnight cruises in which they take over diving and surfacing, maneuver the ship submerged,

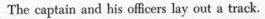

The captain and his officers lay out a track.

and perform as many as possible of the duties that regular ship's officers carry out on watch. They even get to man all stations of the fire control party when practice torpedo attacks are made against other ships.

The experiences the officers share together in school make for lifelong friendships. No outsider can know the difficulties of escape tank training or the thrill of first bringing a submarine alongside the pier for a landing. These friendships mean that in no port where the submariners are stationed will the officer be lonely. There will always be reunions with old friends in store for the visiting submarine officer. Graduation from submarine school is not the time of farewell that saddens so many college graduations. It is almost certain that the submariners will see each other again and again.

The nuclear submarine eagerly awaits its new officer. His arrival has been known for many weeks, and a new face in the wardroom is always welcome. The captain and executive officer have discussed his duty assignments; and the workload of the other officers will soon be lighter. However, qualification in submarines is one of the most important jobs the new man will have during the first year. The guide to qualification is a manual, over an inch thick, crammed with questions and practical requirements varying from demonstrations of how to act as captain to how to shoot practice torpedoes.

During the qualification period the officer will be found climbing about the submarine, tracing out piping, personally operating equipment, standing watches under instruction, and asking questions of everyone. By the end of the year he knows that submarine!

He proves his knowledge and ability by performance at sea and in port before a qualification board consisting of the division commander, a commander who is his skipper's boss, and two other submarine captains. At the end of his qualifying cruise at sea the squadron commander pins the gold dolphins of the submarine officer onto his uniform. He has made the grade and can handle the job of any officer on board except that of the captain himself.

There are other routes to becoming a submarine officer. Some newly commissioned officers go directly to submarine school where those who do well enough are sent on for nuclear-power training. The rest go to diesel-electric submarines but they may be chosen for nuclear-power training after submarine qualification.

Officers who, upon commissioning, go to surface ships may apply after a year for submarine training. Top-quality naval aviators are also welcomed into nuclear-power training and submarine duty, so great has been the expansion of the submarine service.

One might think that school was over for the qualified nuclear submarine officer. True, he will probably be given several years to do the job on board and catch his breath. But there are always new, complicated systems on submarines, and he may need further schooling to learn to operate them.

Submarine sonar, the navigation systems used on ballistic-missile submarines, and weapons systems are examples. Before an officer takes a complex technical job such as weapons officer of a Polaris submarine, he must attend the weapons course at the missile school in Dam Neck, Virginia.

The jobs on board nuclear submarines for officers other than captain and executive officer are prescribed by Navy regulations. There is an operations officer who is responsible for planning sea operations, communications, operation of the sonar, radar and other electronic equipment. The operations officer gives the commanding officer minute-by-minute advice on carrying out complex missions at sea. Under him come the sonar officer and the communications officer.

Navigator is a most important billet. The engineering officer (chief engineer) has several engineer-officer assistants—the main propulsion assistant, the electrical officer, the damage control officer, and the reactor control officer. The supply officer is responsible for ordering, storing, and issuing about 30,000 different kinds of items needed as spare parts. He is also usually the commissary officer who runs the mess (food preparation) for all hands. The weapons officer is boss of the nuclear and conventional armament on board.

Except for the jobs of executive and chief engineer officer, these duties may be changed by the captain as he sees fit, consistent with special training requirements. Often the operations officer is also sonar and communications officer. The duties of both electrical and reactor control officer may be performed by one man.

There are other responsibilities known as collateral duties. These are passed out among the officers and tend to even the workload among them. Diving officer is probably the most important collateral duty. The diving officer takes the dive at battle stations; it is his job to see that the ship is properly rigged for diving upon first proceeding to sea. He makes certain that the variable ballast tanks are filled with the proper amount of water to give the submarine neutral buoyancy upon diving. Under the polar ice, on the first sea trial of a newly built submarine, or on the first dive after the shipyard overhaul, this officer has a particularly heavy responsibility.

Other collateral duties are membership on the crypto board (coding and decoding radio messages), courts-martial, inventory board for medical narcotics and alcohol, voting, sale of savings bonds, information and education, and many more.

Four-hour watches take up a big part of the submarine officer's time. At sea he takes his turn as officer of the deck responsible for controlling the ship's routine and the maneuvering of the ship as well. He also rotates as the engineering officer of the watch.

In port he stands twenty-four-hour watch as duty officer about every sixth day. He gets sleep during the night, but is awakened to make an inspection of the ship every four hours. The executive officer and captain are the only officers who do not stand these watches.

Submarine officers take turns getting the ship underway from the pier and bringing her alongside. Opportunities for the young officers to make torpedo attacks at sea are rotated.

The captain has the full responsibility and authority: here Captain Edward L. Beach of *Triton* takes his ship into port.

After a qualified submarine officer has completed at least two years in an operating submarine, he becomes eligible to be qualified for command of submarines. He must convince his captain that he has all the skills, judgment, and knowledge necessary to be a good skipper. How well does he react in emergencies without help? How does he respond under prolonged tension? What sort of leader is he?

The officer must submit an original thesis on some subject of importance and interest to the Submarine Force. Many valuable new ideas and suggestions have been received from these papers. The thesis is commented upon by the captain and the division commander, and if it is satisfactory it is finally accepted by the squadron commander.

Before the submarine skipper recommends one of his officers for command, he will weigh his qualifications very carefully. He knows that at sea the captain of a submarine stands alone in his responsibility; there is no way to prevent a poor captain from endangering his submarine and her crew. But in most cases the skipper can forward his recommendation to the squadron commander.

A command qualification board is like the board that passes on submarine officer qualification, but now the squadron commander, who holds the rank of captain, is the senior member, and the division commander is the other member. The officer being examined is given a problem at sea which includes making a torpedo attack on another ship. He acts as captain for the day and is observed closely as he goes through drills and makes the landing on return to port.

If the board can honestly say that they would be happy to have the officer in their own organization as captain of a submarine, their recommendation goes to the Chief of Naval Personnel in Washington, D.C., for final approval. An officer qualified to command submarines wears no special insignia, but his official record shows that he is well on the way to achieving actual command at sea.

The next thing he must do is serve well as executive officer of a submarine. The exec is responsible to the captain for everything that goes on in the ship. He sees that the captain's policies and orders are faithfully executed. His way of doing this should inspire confidence and generate enthusiasm. He coordinates and supervises the work of the officers and crew. In the captain's absence he acts for him. It is a difficult and exacting job at best, but it is an important one in which the officer learns much about how a ship should be commanded.

The captain himself is all important to the way his submarine functions. During attacks at periscope depth only he can see, and thus know, what must be done. In an emergency he must function rapidly and effectively or all may be lost.

In the day-to-day life of the ship, his ideas, bearing, speech, and habits set the tone in the wardroom and throughout the ship. One has only to visit a number of submarines to observe how the captain's personality and his degree of competence become stamped on his organization. It is a personal kind of command.

The captain's power to punish his officers and men is relatively weak. No longer does the cat-o'-nine-tails cut into the back of errant sailors. Nor does the captain need to inflict such a punishment. The sailors of today are intelligent and ambitious.

On the captain's judgment rests all officer and enlisted promotion. If he is totally dissatisfied with an officer's performance, he can severely damage, or end, his future in the Navy and cause his disqualification and transfer from submarines, subject at all times to the review and approval of his superiors.

Over enlisted men, his power is no less absolute. Since most men of the submarine service are professionals, or "twenty-year men," the captain's disapproval would be catastrophic.

With such armament the typical nuclear submarine captain finds no need to raise his voice. His authority is unquestioned. It is his custom to do everything possible to help his men achieve recognition. And they in turn do all they can for ship and skipper.

9

LIFE ON BOARD

A LITTLE GIRL recently sent a greeting card to her uncle, a naval officer. She had drawn a gay crayon drawing of a submarine, with its American flag proudly flying. Her caption for the drawing read, "Canned people."

Indeed, this is the image that many people have of life on board a submarine. They ask, "How do you stand it in that confined space with all those others? Don't you feel unbearably closed in just realizing that you can't get out for so long?"

The answer is that submarine crews like their job, do not feel imposed upon, and are amused by these questions. Submarine men are so carefully screened before they go aboard that the chance of a really "mixed-up" case is remote. It is obvious to these well-adjusted sailors that the questioners have no idea of what their outlandish but enjoyable life is really like.

Civilian and Navy psychiatrists worried about the new nuclear submarines because they thought that there *ought* to be a problem. So they came aboard to find it. But the sailors didn't know about any problems.

On one famous nuclear submarine, the crew hugely

enjoyed playing games with a serious-minded psychiatrist sent to find their "problem" and to help solve it. They answered his questions and filled out his questionnaires with calculated, gleeful efforts to confuse the poll. They asked him in every encounter in the passageway, "Doc, why are you on board?" The poor doctor was reported to have left the ship mumbling to himself.

Some people think that life in a submarine is similar to spending weeks at a time in a home bomb shelter. What they fail to realize is that the submarine crew keeps busy. There is great variety to the submariner's life.

When the demands on the men's time for watches, repair work, and battle stations are added up, it can be seen that time does not hang heavy on their hands. But ship's work is not the only thing that keeps the men busy. There is much enjoyable recreation, too.

Special attention is paid to movies. The Navy has a motion-picture service which rents films for showing aboard Navy ships and stations. A submarine can draw one movie for every day she will be away from port. The showings are held in the crew's mess and wardroom at least once a day if the operating schedule permits. On Sundays there may be two movie sessions for the benefit of those on watch who missed a particularly good show.

The movie hour is one of complete relaxation. Plates of cookies and sandwiches and bowls of popcorn and hard candy are passed around and washed down with steaming mugs of the Navy coffee or hot chocolate so dear to the seaman. Soft-drink machines get a work-out.

Sailors make a responsive and enthusiastic audience. Cat calls and hisses greet the villain. Whistles and applause greet the heroine. Between reels light banter is exchanged as cups and plates are refilled.

Cards, chess, cribbage, and acey-ducey are favorite games. Tournaments catch the interest of the whole ship, and, starting with the semifinals, everyone is informed of individual scores over the loudspeaker. Prizes are passed out to the winners.

Books and magazines are in demand. The Navy's library service keeps ships supplied with the newest library editions and paperbacks, and the bookshelves

USS *Nautilus* shows a movie in the dining area. Movies are shown at sea once or twice a day.

always have good variety. Each time the ship is at a Navy base the older books are exchanged for titles not previously carried aboard.

On long cruises and on special holidays when the submarine finds itself away from home, the crew enjoys putting on a show known as happy hour. Fancy dress is often worn. The happy hour will feature all sorts of amusement such as plays, songs, individual acts, and contests. The contests run the gamut from Indian wrestling, pie eating, and juggling, to tallstorytelling, drawing, and poetry.

On one ship the officers, from the captain down, appeared barechested and barefooted in Samoan lavalavas with ink tattoos, bead necklaces, and musical instruments. Then they sang and danced to their own accompaniment for the amusement of the crew.

From this episode it is possible to grasp something of the warmth of the normal relationship between the officers and men. It would be hard to find a situation where superiors and subordinates are in closer daily contact.

It has been said that familiarity breeds contempt. The saying assumes that a man deserves contempt when he is closely scrutinized. Submarines disprove that old saying.

The closer the enlisted man observes the capable young officer, seeing him apply knowledge and reasoning to the problems at hand, the more respect and admiration he can accord him.

The officer in turn sees the inventiveness and craftsmanship of his men displayed daily. He sees their initiative and reliability. When something goes wrong, he will often find it necessary *to order them to stop and to rest.*

Together, the officer and his men undergo the hectic labors of preparing the ship for sea. They endure the long watch when things go wrong and experience the pleasures of movies and happy hours when things go right. They enjoy each other's stories of life back home and of the cruises they have made on other ships. The latest episode in the efforts of a young sailor to get his girl to marry him will be devoured by his shipmates, both officers and men.

That does not mean that the submarine officer does not command. It does mean that his leadership is based more on personal respect and mutual admiration than on the insignia he wears and the commission he holds as an officer. It means a minimum of restrictions on the free life of the submarine crew.

In a surface ship with a large crew it is necessary to issue liberty cards to those enlisted men who have permission to go ashore and to collect the cards when they return to the ship. The men are always lined up and inspected by the officer of the deck before they go ashore to be sure that they are smart-looking.

Such techniques are unnecessary in submarines. The men keep their liberty cards at all times—the ship is too small for a truant not to be missed. Submariners can be relied upon to stay well groomed.

The men can also be relied upon to use a fair share of their time to study. In between watches, many of the crew will be found working on textbooks and manuals which will help them on the next examination for promotion or qualification. Some will be taking correspondence courses that are helpful for promotion, but which are primarily designed to further their education.

Many boys are too immature to buckle down to hard work in high school, and they leave before graduation to join the armed services. In submarines where they serve as seamen or firemen (the lowest enlisted grades) these young men perceive, for the first time, the value of an education. They discover that the United States Armed Forces Institute gives correspondence courses leading to the equivalent of a high school diploma. Getting a basic education is the key to entering advanced training in missiles and nuclear power, and thus fast promotion.

Some submarine men who are high school graduates take college-level correspondence courses or attend extension courses run by colleges, like Harvard, which give college credits. The urge to know more is stimulated by the amount of remarkable equipment aboard ship. And it is helped by the visits of sharp-minded representatives from equipment manufacturers who join the ship to instruct the crew in the use and servicing of their latest models.

The officers conduct classes for the men to meet specific requests. For instance, on one ship college algebra and trigonometry were the favorite subjects during one cruise. On another ship the crew discovered that an officer had studied Russian at the Naval Academy, and he was soon deeply absorbed in teaching Russian classes.

But the time comes when the cry is heard, "Time to set up—let's go!" The men reluctantly collect their working papers and move out of the mess hall to let the mess cooks set up for the next meal. Often the mess call disturbs men who are working over logs or spare-parts' records and accounts; the protests are particularly loud as the men interrupt their labors and pick up their stacks of papers. Yet the crew must be fed.

Submarine crews will not believe that there is better food on board any other kind of ship except a passenger liner. Special money allowances for food are given to submarines to permit a rich and varied diet and to help make up for the lack of sunlight which is so important to good health.

Steaks, roasts, and other expensive cuts of meat served with fresh-frozen vegetables and potatoes are customary. Milk and fresh fruit last for many days after leaving port, and such specialty items as realistic-tasting powdered milk and frozen fruit help fill the void when fresh supplies are exhausted. Fresh bread and desserts such as ice cream and pastries are always available.

Breakfast often features the baker's special coffee cake or doughnuts. Shell eggs are a normal part of the menu for weeks before powdered eggs must make their entry. Dehydrated bacon is one of the marvelous-tasting results of the efforts to reduce space needed for storage—in this case, refrigerator storage. The Navy

The cook prepares "chow" in a gleaming modern galley.

has done great things in boning meat, dehydrating foods without sacrificing taste, and preparing food in the most compressed form. The cooks and bakers vie with each other to please the crew. It is no wonder that many of the ship's company have to exercise and watch their weight.

Exercise is a problem. Different ships solve the problem in different ways. Some use bicycle and rowing machines. Others favor weight-lifting and various

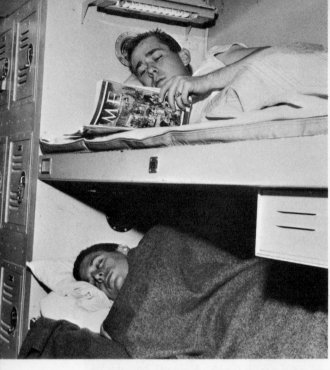

At the end of the day the bunk feels good.

tension machines. One Polaris submarine pioneered an inflatable gym which was set up in the missile compartment between the missile tubes.

There is always sufficient space to do push-ups and deep knee bends. Each quarter year the Navy requires a test of the physical fitness of all personnel under the age of forty, so no one can afford to get soft.

No one can afford to be too sensitive, either. The banter and joking can be playfully rough at times, but the newcomer learns to adjust to it. Practical jokes are not infrequent.

Illness is a rare thing in a submarine, except for colds, which disappear after the first few weeks at sea. The crews have been carefully screened physically.

But occasionally the hospital corpsmen are faced with some grave problems. Doctors are aboard smaller nuclear submarines only for the first year of the ship's life. After that the doctor's advice must be obtained by radio.

Illness is occasionally of the humorous variety. One officer recently came off watch at midnight and went into the pantry to prepare popcorn. It was not until the following morning that his sudden severe illness was discovered to stem from his having mistaken detergent for the oil normally used to make popcorn.

One ship had a doctor who was most interested in keeping everyone aboard, including himself, in perfect trim. Anyone who showed a tendency to gain weight received his advice to cut down at the table. The doctor himself had to fight to control his waistline.

The wardroom pranksters secretly began to snip a little off the doctor's web belt each night while he was asleep. Each morning it seemed to the good doctor that his stomach was expanding against his belt. He compensated at first casually, but then with increasing concern, by eating less at mealtimes. When at last the truth dawned on the hungry doctor many days later, the wardroom officers dissolved in helpless laughter.

Sundays at sea are observed as the Sabbath as much as possible. No unnecessary work is planned, though watches must be stood as usual. A pause comes during the morning; the card games and music from the tape recorder are stopped, and divine services are held. Naturally, attendance is completely voluntary.

Lay leaders conduct the services for the various faiths, depending on the make-up and inclinations of the crew. On some ships the captain serves as the lay leader. Taped services may be used, or the lay leader may lead Bible discussions, or follow services from the "Manual for Lay Leaders." These services mean a great deal to those who participate.

Submarine life is by no means all spent at sea. The antisubmarine nuclear submarine spends about half of her time in port. The crews of the Polaris submarines rotate to give them about half of each year in their home port.

When the submarine is in her home port, there is much work to do, cleaning, repainting, repairing, and taking on spare parts and stores for the next cruise. The submarine needs about three weeks to get in apple-pie order for a long cruise, but it can be done in forty-eight hours in a pinch.

Sailors are a gay lot and their return to port signals family reunions and parties. The whole ship will have a giant picnic or a dinner dance. This is the time for the men to take some leave with pay from the thirty days allowed them each year.

Sports are a favorite form of relaxation and the ship is likely to field several teams playing softball, touch football, and perhaps bowling. The individuals in the crew may enjoy everything from flying private aircraft to stock-car racing, deep-sea fishing, and hunting.

Sailors are great hobbyists, and so the base hobby shops are always humming with activity. The men tinker with their cars, build or refinish furniture, or try their hands at dozens of kinds of handicraft. All the tools are there, and they need to buy only the materials.

The chance to visit foreign ports is welcomed by submarines. Few major sea ports in the non-Communist world remain unvisited by United States submarines. In recent years nuclear submarines have visited Great Britain, France, the Netherlands, Norway, Australia, the Philippines, the Republic of China, Italy, Greece, and other storied lands. They cruise to Bermuda, the Virgin Islands, Puerto Rico, and Malta.

And at these places the submariners enjoy sight-seeing and night life along with American tourists who must spend a great deal for the privilege. There is truth in the saying, "Join the Navy and see the world!"

10

FIGHTING SUBMARINES
AND SURFACE CRAFT

THE AMERICAN INDIAN was a master of the kind of warfare a submarine uses at sea. When hunting, the Indian used stealth and surprise to put an arrow through the heart of the game. On the warpath, the Indian used the same technique against his enemy.

The ship became a submarine and went below the surface of the sea for concealment, just as the Indian left the beaten path and melted into the underbrush. At first, no way was known to see a submarine under water—the camouflage was perfect. But in World War I this curtain was parted just a little.

The use of active sonar in 1918, sending probing, powerful impulses into the water, made it possible for a destroyer to discover a submarine at a range of about a mile. Usually, however, the submarine was able to deliver her torpedo attack before being detected. Then she could be followed and destroyed by far faster surface vessels dropping ashcan-shaped depth charges which sank to explode at a preset depth.

In World War II antisubmarine technique was the same. The German submarines went a little bit faster and deeper than they had twenty years before. Ameri-

126

The USS *Skate* (SSN-578) and USS *Seadragon* (SSN-584) surface together at the North Pole, during under-ice anti-submarine exercises.

can submarines found that Japanese destroyers used passive sonar, listening patiently to noises from the depths and then rushing in to drop depth charges.

Today the slow-sinking depth charge is too inaccurate a weapon to kill a speeding nuclear submarine. Nor can the surface ship rely any longer on being able to outmaneuver and chase down the undersea craft. Rough weather can damage surface ships and force them to slow to a crawl while the submarine at its great depth is unaffected.

The submarine can hear inquiring active sonar pulses dozens of miles away just as she can hear the beating of the propellers of surface ships. Yet they cannot detect the submarine's presence until she gets much closer.

So, Indianlike, the submarine stalks the surface

force it wants to attack, enabled by the high speed and endurance of her nuclear power plant to select the most opportune place and moment to strike.

The submarine may sneak up from behind to fire torpedoes. Astern, the surface-ship sonar is deafened by the boiling wakes and noises from her propellers. The latest submarines need not get close at all. They will be able to fire missiles from great distances into the foe.

The submarine may be on a special mission requiring it to avoid surface craft. As it hears them first, it has only to move out of their way to avoid detection.

These are some of the reasons why the submarine had to learn to fight its own kind. It was necessary to "set a thief to catch a thief." A submarine, particularly a nuclear submarine, has great advantages to aid it in this task. It is very quiet when running slow and hardly makes a sound when its engines stop. With little noise in its ears the sonar can pick up the sounds of a speeding submarine. Moving fast, a nuclear submarine makes far less noise than a surface ship, but it can be heard by another submarine.

Sound beams are deflected or bent by water temperature as they travel in the sea. A deep layer of cold water deflects sound waves from a destroyer's active sonar back up toward the surface, thereby hiding any submarine lurking below. Although destroyers often lower sonar projectors, or transducers, on cables, they cannot be put down nearly as deep as a submarine can dive. Sonar mounted in a submarine goes all the way down to maximum operating depth.

The faint noise of a submarine is also bent by the thermal layers in the sea. The listening, passive sonar of a killer submarine, therefore, often works best deep. When used deeply submerged, the passive sonar is not bothered by the noise of the crashing waves on the surface. What depth to search at, where to look, how fast to go—these questions plague the captain of a nuclear submarine as he patiently awaits his enemy. His world is dark and cold. Every square inch of his patrolling ship is under extremely high pressure. Every sound in the sea is recorded and studied to see if it comes from the enemy.

Aboard the killer submarine, men carry on their routine. Their vigil may last many days. But at any moment there may come the faint rustle that signifies an intruder.

Then instantly the killer is alert. The captain dashes to the attack center and the key members of the fire control party rush in to take their posts. The ship is turned silently toward the noise as the captain studies it intensively.

What is it? Are we sure it isn't a merchant ship? No, it must be a submarine. How fast is she going? In what direction does she head? How far away is she? At what depth does she run?

These are some of the questions that the commanding officer and his fire control team must answer as the killer eases closer to the unsuspecting adversary. No noise must be made that will alert the enemy.

Nothing can be seen. Only the noise is there, now growing a little louder. The noise begins to have distinctive elements that mean much to the practiced ear. Like a dog's unerring nose for its master's scent, the sonarman's sense of hearing for a submarine's sound is well developed—and it is helped by a number of secret devices.

Now the torpedomen move to their stations preparing to fire. The torpedo tube doors swing open.

"He's stopping, Captain! Lost contact!"

Instantly the captain stops the killer submarine and orders all equipment, not absolutely necessary, turned off. Silence falls on the group. Beads of perspiration begin to form on the fire control party's faces.

Nothing happens for some minutes. Then comes the report, "Noise level bearing 319." Dials whirl as the new position of the enemy is fed into computing machines.

"That checks, Captain!" reports the executive officer.

"Final bearing and shoot," orders the captain.

"Set——*shoot!*"

A faint rumble is heard as the first homing torpedo, and then others, leave their tubes and speed toward the target. Now everyone waits breathlessly for an explosion.

"Noise level bearing 063," reports the sonar operator. The captain quickly makes sure that it is not a torpedo gone amuck circling back to smash its launcher.

"Blam——*crash!*" A hit! The sonar operators clutch at their ears, which are ringing from the terrific noise of the explosion. A cheer goes up in the killer submarine.

"Torpedoes coming in from 057!" The skipper suddenly understands there were *two* enemy submarines!

"All ahead flank! Right full rudder! Sound the collision alarm!" The captain desperately begins the violent maneuvers he hopes will cause the enemy torpedoes to miss.

The ship rolls and weaves like a wild thing to avoid the deadly fan of torpedoes now nearly on top of her. Their wakes are visible on the sonar screens.

One torpedo whirs down the side; its propellers are heard clearly through the hull. Another torpedo churns below and aft. They missed! White-faced, the killer's men concentrate on their almost inaudible new foe. No use staying quiet now, they reason; she sees us.

"Echo range! Standby SUBROC!" snaps the captain.

A great blast of noise leaves the bow of the submarine and races through the sea. A circle of light simultaneously leaves the center of the sonar screens and spreads outward like a wave caused by a stone hitting a pond. All at once it leaves a white blob on the screen: the enemy.

"Shoot SUBROC!" cries the captain. For a moment the ship is filled with noise, but the missile springs from the water and all is silent again.

But not for long—the ship suddenly shakes all over in a violent shudder; a terrifying crash makes the ears tingle and the heart pound. The new enemy is dead.

Reloading torpedo tubes, the killer submarine moves carefully away from the area of the blast so as not to suck up any of the radioactively contaminated water into the ship's circulating water system. Now, in the far distance, the killer hears the fast rhythmic beat of surface-ship propellers. They can be heard much farther than those of a submarine because they rotate so fast that little bubbles of water vapor are formed on the trailing edges of the propeller blades. This is called "cavitation." As the bubbles collapse, they produce a crackling noise.

Submarines' propellers would cavitate and make loud noises too if they were run fast at the surface or a shallow depth. But as the submarine goes deeper,

An artist's conception of the firing of a Polaris missile through a hole in the polar ice pack.

the pressure of the water becomes increasingly great, so that water-vapor bubbles cannot form. Submarines can run deep, even at top speed, with silent propellers.

The killer submarine also hears the high-pitched "ping" of the enemy surface-ship sonars. Destroyers attracted by the nuclear blast are coming to search the area.

The killer's captain reviews his mission. He is to sink enemy submarines as first choice, but any warship is fair game. He turns to attack. The "bong-bong-bong!" of the general alarm brings the crew to battle stations.

Four enemy ships have formed a line abreast to come into the vicinity of the killer. The captain takes sonar bearings on each ship and watches his team use its instruments to plot the positions with precision. The enemy is many miles away, zigzagging on a base course of about 136 degrees True, making about 18 knots.

The captain swiftly makes his plan. He will increase speed and move to attack a destroyer on the end of the line. Unlike enemy submarines, surface ships at search speed cannot hear over their own noise, and so they will not be alerted by the racing submarine engines.

In an hour the submarine is within ten miles of the wing destroyer. Slowing down, the captain warily lets the searching line go by so that his ship can come up astern of the wing destroyer where her sonar is weakest. Then he increases speed to overtake the line from the rear.

All is working perfectly. The torpedo tube outer doors go open. The captain toys with the idea of going up for a look at his target through the periscope.

"No, that would give the destroyer a chance to detect me with his sonar above the thermal layer, or even with aircraft, if they spot my periscope. I don't have to have a look," he reasons.

"Captain, the target aspect is changing. They are turning!" calls the sonar operator.

Immediately the captain stops the engines. He can hear better that way, and if the enemy turns all the way around it will give more time to shoot by slowing down the rate at which the submarine and destroyer are closing in on each other.

The noises from the target are studied tensely; there is no doubt that the targets have turned almost ninety degrees to the left to sweep out another area. With this turn the torpedo range is very good, but there is increased chance of the killer's being detected. There is no time to be lost. A salvo of torpedoes is sent speeding toward the nearest destroyer. At this distance it will be a number of minutes before they can hit. In the meantime the torpedo tubes are reloaded.

"Captain, they are turning toward us again and speeding up!" reports sonar.

This turn could cause all the torpedoes to miss, and all the destroyers are rushing down on the killer like an express train. The captain bitterly regrets his decision not to use the nuclear-tipped SUBROC. He was conserving them for use against submarine targets. It is too late to shoot one now—the targets are so close that the killer herself might be damaged by the atomic blast.

"Blam——*crash!*"

"We got him!" yells the captain in relief. "All ahead flank; I'm going to get right up close to him for protection. Let's hope that he doesn't sink too rapidly."

The next few minutes are critical. If the other destroyers get contact they may launch a nuclear-tipped missile. But the lucky killer manages to slip in near the crippled, sinking destroyer.

The other destroyers go charging on, searching for the culprit. Now the captain angles his ship steeply upward and levels off at periscope depth.

"Up periscope," commands the skipper.

Nearby lies the destroyer, burning and low in the water, her stern completely submerged. A hasty look around reveals two destroyers circling back and another heading straight for the sinking ship.

"Quick! Let's get a setup on this guy and shoot," shouts the captain, and he pours out a torrent of orders.

The ship shivers as more torpedoes are launched. Immediately the captain dodges his ship around close behind the sinking destroyer. The noise of the torpedoes is lost in the destroyer's horrible cracking, breaking-up noises that surround the submarine.

Two white plumes shoot up high above the second destroyer, and seconds later the crashing explosions are heard through the hull.

But suddenly the submarine is nearly shattered by a fearsome explosion. She rolls on her beam, light bulbs are shattered, and everyone is knocked down. The lights go out and the dim battle lanterns blink on. Water spurts from cracked or broken pipes in a dozen places. The captain, bleeding from a severe cut on his forehead, sits dazed and half-conscious on the deck. The executive officer assumes command. "Take her deep," he shouts.

But the steam propulsion has been lost and the ship only creeps downward. Just before she leaves periscope depth, the executive officer sees what has happened. The close destroyer has blown up. A towering pillar of smoke marks her final position. Wreckage falls into the water. Now the odds have changed. The killer is badly hurt and will have to fight for her life against the remaining two destroyers if they attack. War is not all take and no give, even for submarines with nuclear power.

11

SOME UNUSUAL JOBS

SUBMARINES have landed spies and saboteurs often in wartime. Doubtless the Communists could land them tonight in countries where the struggle for freedom is in progress, if it suited their purpose. Since its approach cannot be detected by radar, the submarine is better for this task than the airplane.

To be prepared in case of war, the United States Navy practices this kind of mission as a matter of routine. The assignment to practice night landings is rotated among the submarines.

The night picked to land spies must be a black one. The moon, rising suddenly over a hill, could lend unwelcome illumination to the scene.

It is best to pick a sloping beach, close enough to deep water so that the submarine can remain submerged until the last minute. Breakers, if they are heavy enough, will swamp our agents' boat; choosing a landing place protected from the prevailing wind is an important part of the plan.

Before landing agents, the admiral's staff studies the possible landing areas, the weather forecast, the moon tables, known enemy installations near the landing site, and every factor that could make a difference. There is never enough knowledge about the area. In a real war operation, the files would be combed to locate citizens who have lived in the enemy country. Their memories would be challenged by endless questions about the beach area. What years ago was a casual vacation at the seashore could now furnish vital information to the United States.

An actual look at the beach area is often needed. If an aircraft flies over it, it may be shot down; in any case an airplane would arouse the suspicions of the enemy forces. So a submarine reconnaissance mission is scheduled to examine the two places which have been tentatively selected as the best landing area.

In broad daylight, as near to the shore as the depth of the water will allow, the nuclear submarine slowly cruises along. At frequent intervals the slender periscope is raised, a photograph is taken, and the periscope disappears. It is virtually impossible for the periscope to be sighted from the shore, but the captain must be careful to watch for aircraft, patrol ships, or small craft.

Back at the home base, the photographs are greatly enlarged, and every minute detail is studied. At last the landing place is chosen, and the agents themselves make their final plans.

It is not long before the submarine cruises past the objective once again. The agents make a final study of the terrain and then rest for their busy night.

After dark the submarine surfaces silently and moves as close as possible to shore. A rubber boat is inflated and the men disappear paddling into the night. Quickly, the submarine returns to deep water and submerges, her mission accomplished.

In some areas the patrol is so intense that the submarine cannot surface, even at night, for fear of being detected by radar. Here it will be necessary to send the operatives ashore in frogmen suits. With the submarine still submerged, but close to shore, the agents go up into the same escape trunk that would be used by the submarine crew in an emergency. The lower door is closed behind them. A valve is turned and sea water gushes in, rising quickly up to the level of their mouths as they swallow to equalize the increasing pressure in their eardrums.

Now the water is just over the top of the side door of the escape trunk, and, with the pressure the same inside and outside, the door is opened to the sea. The frogmen leave and begin the long swim ashore.

These agents may eventually have to be evacuated, and a submarine can do this work, too. It is a more dangerous assignment, because the enemy may intercept the communications needed to make the arrangements and may set a trap for the agents. Rescuing men from right under the enemy's nose is a nuclear-submarine specialty and carries on the work done by submarines during World War II when there were many such successful submarine rescues. Eighty-six submarines rescued 504 American flyers; the USS *Tigrone* alone accounted for 31.

When their aircraft was damaged, the aviators ditched it at a secret, invisible, prearranged pickup point just off the enemy shore. Taking to their life raft, the pilot and crew would suddenly see a submarine surfacing from almost underneath them. In minutes the downed aviators would be on board, and the submarine would be safely submerged once more.

In some instances the pilots landed under enemy fire. If they could not paddle clear, the submarines towed them to sea with a periscope.

Less glamorous (and rather unpopular with submariners) is the mission of supplying or evacuating cutoff outposts in areas where our other forces dare not go. There was a great deal of this kind of work in the last great war, and the nuclear submarine is prepared to do it again, even though it is not especially designed for the job.

Examples of what might have to be done in the future can be shown by past experience. The *Seawolf* delivered 37 tons of machine gun ammunition to Corregidor when that island in Manila Bay was besieged in 1942. The *Swordfish* then took President Quezon of the Philippines and his party of nine from Corregidor and later also rescued the United States High Commissioner, F.B. Sayre, and his party of twelve.

The list of World War II special missions of supply and evacuation is a long one. The *Amberjack* delivered 5,000 gallons of aviation gasoline and some 200-pound bombs to Tulagi. The *Trout* brought out 20 tons of Philippine gold and silver from Corregidor. The *Narwal* delivered 70 tons of ammunition and stores and then evacuated 28 women from Mindanao, Philippine Islands. Many, many more such missions were conducted in the enemy-held islands of the western Pacific.

The Japanese navy used submarine supply for their island bases more and more as the American advance cut them off. By the end of the war, submarines were the only means of supporting these isolated, bypassed garrisons.

The German U-boats brought several extremely valuable cargoes to Hitler's Germany. These contained rare items desperately needed by the German war industry, which the Allied blockade had cut off.

The use of submarines to land raiding parties is another type of special mission that would be sure to fall to the nuclear submarine in wartime. The famous "Carlson's Raiders," a 121-man Marine commando team, was landed to raid Makin Island by the submarines *Argonaut* and *Nautilus* in 1942. This raid came after the Pearl Harbor disaster and the Philippine surrender at a time when American morale needed a boost.

Nautilus was at it again with the *Narwal* in May 1943. The two submarines landed 214 Army scouts on Attu Island in the Aleutian chain during our preparations to take that island. Knowing that his opponent can land small groups of men undetected on his coast for a quick raid is enough to give the enemy the jitters. The raiders can be landed, strike hard (perhaps with nuclear charges), and be back on board their submarines within hours. The enemy must tie down many men to try to protect himself against such an attack.

The nuclear submarine's ability to remain undetected can serve other purposes too. Patrolling off enemy ports, submarines can be used as expert eyes to report the passage of enemy fleets or to survey the weather just before an attack.

Wartime odd jobs are matched by many fascinating peacetime chores. The nuclear submarine was an American "first," and so it is an object of intense interest both at home and abroad.

Good-will cruises are great fun for the submarine and its hosts in foreign lands. The United States Atomic Energy Act cloaks the reactor plant in secrecy, but this does not prevent officially authorized foreign visitors from touring parts of the ship. They have often been taken to sea for a demonstration trip as well.

Even if the reactor compartment door remains sealed, the advantages a ship gains from nuclear power can be dramatically shown. The King and Queen of Greece, members of the British Parliament, cabinet members of various countries, admirals and generals, and important persons of all walks of life have held their breath for a moment as their sleek underwater craft plunged in a deep dive toward the bottom. Braced against the nearest fixed object they eyed the descending depth gauge in wonder.

Then, at the captain's command, the ship's bow swung up toward the surface and the guests now leaned far forward to keep from falling. At this speed one could imagine the ship leaping from the water like a mad whale in a gigantic foaming splash.

But the disciplined submarine levels off abruptly and turns to port with agile ease. As she lists sharply to

A commander in chief visits a Polaris submarine. President Eisenhower on the *Patrick Henry* with Vice Admiral W. F. Raborn who was in charge of the special Navy group that developed the Polaris missile.

port, the yachtsmen note the inward heel with surprise since surface craft heel the other way in a turn. The nuclear submarine obeys the same rules as did the old dirigible, which in many respects it resembles.

Submariners enjoy the opportunity to see and speak to these famous personalities. It is good to be able to show them such a marvelous machine. They in turn take obvious pleasure in the show. Usually special efforts are made by the foreign hosts to show the crew of the visiting submarine a good time.

Back in the United States there are often oppor-

tunities to see distinguished persons. Heads of industry, congressional leaders, and presidents of the United
States all take time out to look over the latest nuclear
submarines.

There is even a chance for the crew to take families
and friends out for short cruises. These outings are
always gay events and are eagerly awaited by wives
and youngsters over twelve years old. Brothers and
girlfriends are welcomed, too. Most times there will
be so many waiting to take the ride that the ship will
have to make both a morning and afternoon cruise
in order to give everyone a chance to ride on board.

At sea there is an opportunity for families and
friends to look through the periscope while submerged, to listen to the weird sounds of fish and ships
over the sonar, to steer the ship and maneuver it a bit
while submerged, and to do the hundred other unusual, exciting things that they have heard so much
about.

One thing is sure to come from the "friend and family cruise." That is a feeling of increased respect for
the husband, father, or friend, gained by seeing him
do the complicated, demanding work on board his
ship. But what about a look for those who don't know
a crew member?

There is a way for the general public to see inside
these expensive ships that their taxes have bought.
Television and movie crews come down occasionally
to record scenes for their viewers. Their bright lights
and bulky camera equipment squeeze on somehow
amid all the submarine's own equipment.

Sailors make self-conscious actors whose amateur status cannot be hidden. So professionals may arrive to do most of the work while the ship's crew serve as extras. If a comely young actress or two come aboard, the ship's company is agog.

The actresses will have no difficulty finding escorts after hours, but well over half of the crew of a nuclear submarine, and nearly all of the officers, are married. However, some submarines have been given jobs that call for a bachelor crew.

The salt-water oceans of the world are less known in many respects than the vaster ocean of space about our planet. Now that so much attention is being paid to submarines it is necessary to study the interior of the seas. What better vehicle could be chosen than the submarine itself?

After a submarine is selected for an oceanographic mission, a call for single men is announced. Before long the ship's company is one long stag line from bow to stern. These men will take their ship on a cruise several years long, roaming over the world on a prearranged timetable.

The crew follows a rigid routine, collecting data on such things as salinity, temperature, currents, bottom contours, marine life, sonar conditions, and many other items. The Navy has scientific contracts with such distinguished organizations as the Scripps Institution of Oceanography at La Jolla, California, and Woods Hole Oceanographic Institution at Woods Hole, Massachusetts. Oceanographers take the Navy data, add it to their own, and furnish the Navy with

The bathyscaphe, *Trieste*, set a new record in deep diving.

invaluable information about conditions under the seas. Much of our knowledge of how to use sonar has been gained in this way.

Scientific investigations are also carried out at home to perfect the submarine and its weapons. For example, what happens when a submarine is subjected to the battering forces of a near-miss explosion? To help answer that question, massive depth charges are exploded at precise distances from nuclear submarines. Yes, the crew is aboard!

The submarine steams along and when she is at the

proper distance from the explosive charge, her captain gives the order—"Fire!" A great plume of tormented white water rises toward the sky. Dead fish by the thousands float to the surface.

Aboard the submarine there is damage, but not severe damage. In minutes the crew has isolated leaks and begun repairs. Notes are made of all defects so that designs can be improved to make the ship more shock-resistant.

Tests of submarine equipment go on around the clock. Nuclear submarines act as targets for new weapons fired by other nuclear submarines and surface ships. They may work against each other to try out the latest ideas for improving sonar equipment. Unusual services of this kind take up a great deal of the time of the submarines of the fleet.

Inventors and engineering firms bring forward new ideas for undersea warfare almost faster than they can be evaluated by the submarine force. Some priority has to be established or our nuclear submarines would do nothing but test gadgetry. Various agencies in Washington, led by the Office of the Chief of Naval Operations, assign these priorities because the greater part of the submarine's time must be reserved for realistic training at sea so that the fleet is ready to fight *now* with *present* weapons.

If variety is what keeps life interesting, the submariner is to be envied. The people he sees, the places he visits, and the jobs he does are extremely varied. Small wonder that telling "sea stories" is a favorite pastime of old submariners.

12

POLARIS ON GUARD

THE FIRST LIGHT of dawn over Scotland reveals a smooth, low-lying shape plunging in through the cold whitecaps of the entrance to the River Clyde. Water rushes back over her bow and cascades against the foot of the sail. Her sail is dark gray. No numbers can be seen beneath the sturdy sail planes. From the shore, no one is visible on her deck or bridge. An American Polaris submarine is returning from patrol.

Inside the ship, the routine is magically changed. Excitement tinges everything; after weeks submerged, the prospect of shore leave and home makes every eye shine with delight, and pride, too, after a successful patrol. As usual all sixteen missiles were ready to shoot more than 95 per cent of the time. Fifteen of the sixteen were ready 99.9 per cent of the period.

The ship glistens after two days of intensive "field day." The crew is decked out in clean, pressed uniforms for the entry into port. Laughter comes easily, even at old jokes retold for the hundredth time on the cruise. Tall tales of past leaves and boasts of the expected gala time ashore are heard.

There is activity aboard the submarine tender at
148

Holy Loch, too. The mother ship's boats leave their nests at the booms on the side, where the submarine will berth and move to the boat booms at the tender's stern. The booms on the side then swing in and are lashed down by young seamen under the watchful eye of a chief boatswain's mate.

Tender-repair officers study the latest work reports of progress on the two Polaris submarines already alongside. They, too, must be kept on schedule; and a new, impatient customer is approaching.

A repair conference has already estimated the amount of work required to refit the newcomer. All that remains to do is to find out about the small items not worth reporting by radio and to get to work on her. But, except for the most urgent things, real work by the tender will not begin that day.

Polaris submarines are operated by two complete ship's companies. They are called Blue Crew and Gold Crew after the colors of the Navy uniform. The Blue Crew is now eating breakfast on board the mother ship, awaiting arrival of their submarine.

The Blue Crew came by military air transport the evening before. After their last patrol they had gone back for their leave and training period to New London, Connecticut, their home port. Special schools there teach crew members how to operate and maintain the submarine's gear at sea. Now the Blue Crew is rested, retrained, and ready to go to sea once more.

The boat gong strikes sharply to announce the departure of the squadron commander. He is accompanied by the Blue commanding officer who will greet

USS *Proteus*, a submarine tender, loads a Polaris missile into a submarine (left) in the Holy Loch, Scotland.

the submarine in the river and then go on board to get firsthand reports of the mission just completed. As the boat curves away from the tender's side, the United States flag fluttering from its stern catches the rays of the early morning sun.

On the tender, the mail room has nearly finished the task of assembling the mail for the 133 persons on board the arriving submarine. In the space of two months there is a big accumulation of personal letters. There is a huge stack of official mail for the ship. The

ship's officers sometimes think that every staff officer
in the Navy feels compelled to tell them how to do
their jobs or to ask them for information.

In the lower decks of the tender, the orderly piles
of fresh provisions grow. Milk, eggs, vegetables, fruits,
and cheese will be a welcome change for these men
from the depths. The ship's store prepares for a busy
day of dispensing shaving supplies, stationery, and
small presents for girlfriends or families.

From the tender's bridge a first glimpse of the gray
ship can be seen as she rounds the headland into the
Holy Loch. Going slowly now, the submarine's bow is
soon dry enough to permit the deck force to go down
and prepare the topside for mooring to the tender.

The men carry wrenches to loosen the clamps that
secure the mooring cleats and hold the deck lockers
closed. From two lockers the capstan heads are removed and installed on deck in their operating positions. Jack staff and flagstaff are brought forth and
inserted into their sockets; no flag will fly from them
until the first mooring line is over to the tender.

Now the streaming colors fly from a short pole at
the after end of the sail. Above the ensign is a long,
thin streamer which looks like a sliver of the American
flag with one row of stars and one red and one white
stripe. It is the commission pennant that is flown by
all United States Navy ships in commission. A sailor
replaces it with the squadron commander's pennant—
a white, swallow-tailed flag with blue borders at top
and bottom, and a blue numeral, 14, emblazoned in
the center. It is hoisted when the commodore (as

squadron commanders are called by courtesy) comes on board.

On the submarine's bridge the skipper has given the task of making the landing to the officer of the deck, and as the submarine nears the tender, the "old man" climbs up onto the top of the sail to see better. Only the raised periscopes give him something to hang onto.

Smoothly the big ship glides up to her berth. Her size is remarkable: about 7,000 tons—as large as many World War II cruisers. She is more than four times the size of United States diesel-electric submarines. A quiet order from the officer of the deck, barely audible to those lining the rails of the tender, and the great submarine begins to churn the water in reverse. The submarine slows gradually to a stop.

A chorus of shouts now rings out as Blue and Gold crews greet each other while their captains look on indulgently. "Monkey fists," weights wrapped with cord and attached to a heaving line, sail over to be grabbed and pulled in by the sailors of the tender. The mooring lines start over; when the first one is in hand a whistle is sounded, the streaming colors come down, the blue-spangled Union Jack is hoisted forward, and a large ensign is run up aft.

It is not long before the transfer of the ship from one crew to the other is in full swing. The latest word on the performance of the equipment is exchanged. Every effort must be made to pass along each scrap of information that might later be needed. In many cases the gear is actually given a demonstration run for the relieving crew. In a few days most of the tired

Ceremony is a part of Navy life. Captain H. E. Shear, Blue skipper of USS *Patrick Henry*, prepares to turn over the ship to the Gold captain.

Gold Crew will be winging across the Atlantic for home, although some of them may spend their leave touring Europe.

As soon as the relief is complete there will be just time for a party or two ashore for the Gold Crew attended by a scattering of people from the tender, the squadron staff, and the other submarines. But the Blues will be hard at work getting their ship ready for the voyage. For not all of this work is done by the tender. Much is done by the crews themselves, who dismount equipment for preventive maintenance and make minor repairs.

Some of the missiles are removed and replaced by new ones in accordance with the rotation policy. Torpedoes are also exchanged. The huge stores of food required to feed a Polaris crew for over sixty days, and longer if need be, must be brought aboard and stowed for ready access. As the spare parts to replace those used during the last patrol come aboard, they are logged and carefully stowed. With so many thousands of parts it would be easy to lose some if the stowage system was not followed exactly. These and a myriad of other duties fill the Blue Crew's time during the three weeks of refit.

Before the ship sails on her patrol, two more big things must be accomplished: the *fast cruise*, and the underway test and training period. The fast cruise is simply a cruise while moored fast to the tender. Steam is raised and for several days the ship's company works the kinks out of the ship and themselves. Casualty drills and refresher training of all kinds are conducted while the equipment that has just been repaired is minutely observed in operation.

Next the ship gets underway for several days and goes through shakedown training at sea to be sure that everything is in perfect order. Torpedo attacks will be made against other ships to make certain that the Polaris submarine is prepared to carry out its secondary mission of antisubmarine warfare after the big missiles have been fired.

And the Blue Crew must be ready to defend themselves if attacked. If an enemy submarine discovers them and makes a hostile move, the Blues would know how to deal with the aggressor.

Now all is in readiness. A last letter home, a final handclasp, and the submarine is away to dive off Scotland and commence patrol.

The expected storm has hit the Scottish coast. As the ancient hills astern disappear in a driving, icy rain blown by the wind almost parallel to the sea, the Polaris submarine rolls heavily. Below, the crew hangs on grimly, awaiting the diving alarm.

The navigator notes the increasing soundings and fixes the ship's position on the chart. At last, he reports having reached diving position to the captain.

"Oogh! Oogh!" goes the alarm. The steel monster settles. Air roars from the tanks as they fill with water to take her down. At 100 feet the ship is trimmed at slow speed. Water is pumped until the ship can hover with no way on. Already the rolling is quenched considerably. It is slower and much more gentle.

Deeper the submarine plunges and increases speed, heading for her secret patrol area. Checks of the missiles, fire control equipment, and navigational apparatus are going on as a matter of routine. Though not in the patrol area, this ship can give assurance that her weapons will land where ordered even if they arrive a day or so later than those from submarines already on station. If given the order to attack, it would be virtually impossible for the enemy to locate her or stop her from completing her terrible mission.

The captain who might have to order the death of millions of human beings, men, women, and children, has faced his heavy responsibility. He must carry out his orders and will do so. The Polaris submarine is designed to prevent war by presenting a prospective aggressor with the certainty of retaliation and de-struction in case of attack on the United States.

By law the only person who can order the nuclear-tipped Polaris missile fired is the President of the United States. Transmission of the President's decision to the submarines at sea would be breathtakingly swift, as has been proved by the delivery of practice messages. But what if some submarine captain went insane and believed that he had received the order to shoot when in fact none had been issued? Would this not start the very destruction of the civilized world that Polaris was built to prevent?

The answer is that the captain cannot fire the missile on his own order alone. His executive officer must agree. And there are other secret safeguards as well.

A high premium is placed on the maturity and ability of the captain and his second-in-command as they help to preside over the safety of the world in general and the United States of America in particular. One may hope that Soviet Russia exercises similar care in establishing safeguards.

These thoughts do not trouble the crew, however. They are familiar with their responsibility and it does not awe them. Work effectively rubs out awe.

The most important duty of the Polaris submarine, besides being ready at all times to fire accurately on

The Polaris submarine, USS *Lafayette* (SSBN-616), slides down the ways following her christening by Mrs. John F. Kennedy on May 8, 1962. The *Lafayette* is the first nuclear submarine designed to fire the new 2,500-mile range Polaris.

targets assigned, is to remain undetected. It is relatively easy to do this, but submarines take no chances. Contact with merchant ships or naval vessels is viewed with suspicion and is avoided.

Each contact is carefully reported. Since submarines on patrol take care to operate in international waters at all times, any concerted attempt to locate them would be highly significant. If they were located, there might be even a local war at sea if the enemy tried to wipe out the potent submarines at their doorsteps.

Any such war at sea would have unpredictable consequences—it could lead directly to World War III. But this will not happen if the submarines can successfully defend themselves. And we are sure that they can do exactly that.

On patrol frequent drills are held in which the submarine is considered to be under attack. Torpedoes are readied in the tubes, and the only thing simulated is actual firing. There is little doubt that these remarkable ships could give a good account of themselves against a foe.

The radio room is in constant touch with headquarters of the Commander in Chief, United States Atlantic Command. This officer is a full admiral (four stars) in the United States Navy, who serves as the Unified Commander under the Joint Chiefs of Staff for the Atlantic Ocean. He has command of all Army, Navy, and Air Force units within his area.

He also sees that news of the latest doings from home are relayed to the men on patrol. Not only is the

international and national news sent, but the news of
the families, and even personal messages from loved
ones, come over the radio. The radio serves as a warm
human link with home, *but the same link could carry
the order to fire.*

13

EXPLORING THE ARCTIC
BY SUBMARINE

COMMANDER EUGENE P. WILKINSON, who was the first captain of the pioneer nuclear-powered submarine *Nautilus*, wanted to explore the Arctic Ocean with his remarkable new ship. He made and remade his plans, but so many urgent projects and tests were scheduled for the *Nautilus* that he never got the chance to take her north. The second captain of the *Nautilus*, Commander William R. Anderson, was also keen to show what a submarine, which needed no outside air to run its engines, could do under Arctic conditions. Commander Anderson found that a considerable amount was known about the Arctic Ocean and its ice pack.

The great ice-covered ocean at the top of the world lies between North America and the Soviet Union. It had always proved impassable to warships. After many expeditions had penetrated part way into the mass of moving ice, Fridtjof Nansen, a Norwegian, froze his ship, the *Fram*, into the ice off Severnaya Zemlya Island in 1893. Borne by the ice, the 128-foot three-masted schooner had drifted to a distance of only 350 miles from the North Pole by March 1895. Nansen and a companion trekked by dog sledge to within 225 miles of the Pole.

The *Fram* would have been crushed in the ice like the ill-fated *Jeanette* in 1881, had she not been specially constructed with sloping, dishlike sides and a wide 36-foot beam. By the spring of 1896 the *Fram* was free off Spitsbergen and came triumphantly home to Norway in August of that year. The expedition brought back a huge store of information about the Arctic.

The North Pole has since been reached by Rear Admiral Robert E. Peary, United States Navy, in 1909, flown over by Rear Admiral Richard E. Byrd, United States Navy, and Floyd Bennett, in 1926, and camped upon by Otto Schmidt, Soviet Union, who landed a plane there in 1937 and drifted for nine months before being picked up off Jan Mayen Island. Since World War II, drifting ice stations have been used more extensively by scientists of the Soviet Union than by those of the United States.

It was known that beyond the shallow continental shelf, the water in the polar basin averaged more than 12,000 feet deep. The shelf extends out 100 miles north of Alaska and is about 700 miles wide in places off the Eurasian shore. But there was still much to be discovered, and it could best be done by ships which go faster than a drifting ice station.

Over a five-year period, from 1957 to 1962, the United States Navy launched a headlong submarine attack on the remaining Arctic mysteries and furnished convincing proof that nuclear submarines can operate in the Arctic with ease. First, Commander Anderson took the *Nautilus* farther north than the *Fram* had penetrated. He was within 180 miles of the North Pole in September 1957, when the failure of navigational instruments forced the *Nautilus* to grope her way home. Undaunted, Anderson crossed the Arctic Ocean from west to east the next year, reaching the North Pole on August 3, 1958.

Only nine days later Commander James Calvert took the nuclear submarine *Skate* across the North Pole and pioneered the art of surfacing through the ice. In March 1959, the *Skate* returned to the North Pole to surface there. It was the first time that any submarine had done this. But what made the cruise even more remarkable was that the submarine surfaced through thick ice in the Arctic winter night on instruments alone.

Early the next year the nuclear submarine *Sargo*, under Lieutenant Commander John H. Nicholson, sailed to the North Pole from Hawaii through the Bering Strait. The *Sargo* refined the technique of surfacing through thick ice in total darkness and was the first ship to use an iceberg detector to avoid deep draft ice over the continental shelf.

In August 1960, the nuclear-powered *Seadragon*, under the command of the author of this book, showed that the iceberg detector, the other electronic equipment, and the techniques of Anderson, Calvert, and Nicholson could be used to steer a submerged submarine through the famed Northwest Passage and

The USS *Skate* surfaces at the Pole. The two crew members standing on the ice are getting samples of the ice for testing.

that ships could operate safely under the ice in close proximity to shoals, islands, and icebergs. The *Seadragon* was the first ship of any kind to go through the Canadian archipelago by way of the ice-clogged Parry Channel, and the first submarine to go under icebergs.

In July 1962 the *Seadragon*, now under Commander Charles D. Summitt, returned to the Arctic Ocean and there met the *Skate*, under Commander Joseph L. Skoog. They conducted the first mock combat under the polar ice, and fired a number of exercise torpedoes at each other. For the first time two submarines surfaced together at the North Pole. On this voyage the *Skate* was the first submarine to use the narrow passage between Greenland and Canada; she returned from the Arctic Ocean via the route opened in 1960 by the *Seadragon.*

There is a thrill in attempting to do what has never been done before. It is both a challenge and a high adventure, but it is also hard work for the crew and those who fit out the submarine for the task. One cannot just take a submarine and sail north.

The first problem that had to be solved by the *Nautilus* was that of navigation. Her compasses had proved unequal to the challenge when they did not work properly after a brief power failure far up north under the ice. Another system had to be found.

An inertial navigation system from a missile proved to be just the thing. With it the submarine can cruise for many days under the ice without a look at the heavens and yet maintain a sufficiently accurate position to find her way across the Arctic Ocean.

There are many openings in the pack ice in the summer. The wind works the ice so that it breaks and forms *polynyas,* a Russian word meaning open areas of water. Even in winter the polynyas exist in a form called "skylights," ice which is frozen to a thickness of only several feet.

The thickness of the Arctic ice varies, but 6 to 15 feet is the general rule. Under pressure from the wind, the thick floes are pushed over one another. When this happens the pressure from the top floe pushes the bottom one deeper in the water, forming "pressure ridges." These ridges can extend down more than 100 feet from the surface, although the average thickness is considerably less, about 40 to 50 feet.

What would happen if a fire sent clouds of toxic smoke billowing through the ship? Suppose there was no hole in the ice through which to surface? These were some of the possible hazards the men of the *Nautilus* faced. As they sailed to the Pacific for their famous crossing, the crew fought a severe, smoky fire in the engine room. Oil-soaked insulation on the turbines caught fire, and heat from the turbines kept re-

During a period of low visibility, Commander W. R. Anderson stands on the bridge of the USS *Nautilus* as he looks for a spot deep enough safely to submerge the ship for the passage under the North Pole.

igniting the fire each time it was put out. The fight lasted for hours.

As a result of this experience, the ingenious crew of the *Nautilus* designed an emergency breathing mask and an air-distribution system that removed the worst fear of fire under the ice. With these masks on, the entire crew can breathe pure air directly from the banks of compressed air usually used for blowing the main ballast tanks. This air can sustain them for a day or longer—plenty of time to put out a fire and remove the smoke with the regular air revitalization gear.

How could the crew know how far the ship was from the ice above? This was an easy problem which had already been solved. All that had to be done was to mount a fathometer upside down on deck. The fathometer is usually used to take soundings of the depth of water under the keel. A sonar pulse is bounced from the bottom. Since the speed of sound in water is known, it is a simple matter to time the echo and cal-culate the distance. And it is just as simple to calculate the distance to the ice overhead. By comparing that distance with the depth of the ship, as determined by the water pressure, the thickness of the ice can be computed.

For good measure the *Nautilus* brought along a sub-marine underwater television set that showed the first views of the underside of the ice. While it was by no means perfect, it gave the men a shadowy idea of what lay overhead. By the time the *Seadragon* made her cruise in 1960, the television set had been im-proved, and the pictures were often remarkably clear.

However, the water is not clear in many parts of the ocean and visibility varies from very good to very poor in the Arctic. At night one can see nothing by television.

In order to aid the *Skate* and later submarines to surface in the ice pack, a small-object-locating sonar called a polynya delineator was designed by experts of the United States Navy Electronic Laboratory at San Diego, California. The polynya delineator indicates the shape of a polynya, and this makes it easier for the skipper to maneuver the ship up into a polynya. The delineator also enables the skipper to see dangerous pieces of ice and avoid them.

Being in a nuclear submarine beneath the ice pack is hardly different from being in one anywhere else. True, the water is colder—about 29° F. Small drops of condensation form here and there where the bare metal of the hull cannot be insulated. The long summer sunlight enables the ship to have a twenty-four-hour TV view of the ice. And while the upward fathometer traces out the profile of the ice overhead, life goes on in the submarine without any change.

There is always the knowledge that one *must* find a place to surface should there be an emergency requiring it. This is a problem that airplane pilots must also face. But if the craft is under control, the possible need for emergency landing or surfacing does not intrude itself into the normal consciousness of the pilot or skipper.

Surfacing is an intricate team effort that requires considerable skill. It takes about 40 to 50 minutes to get up to the surface once a polynya or skylight is located with the fathometer, but it is worth all the effort to see the amazing panorama above the Arctic waters. Let us see how it is done.

While the ship is steaming along deep, the fathometer trace suddenly rises, and the jagged line runs smooth and level. If the line stays smooth and level for 150 yards, the officer of the deck who is watching the fathometer knows that a polynya or skylight is overhead.

After calling the captain and "polynya-plotting party," the officer of the deck slows down and turns the ship in a simple circling maneuver called a "Williamson turn" that brings her back to the polynya.

The captain now assumes the conn. Slowing down further, he orders the ship brought up to a shallow depth. From all sides come chanted reports: the distance to the polynya from the plot; the thickness of the ice overhead from the fathometer; the speed through the water from the electronic log. He can see the instruments that tell the ship's depth, the angle on the ship, and the depth of water under the keel.

Slowly the submarine slides under the opening; the TV shows sparkling water overhead. The submarine is brought to a halt by reversing the propulsion. The captain raises the periscope to look around at the jagged masses of blue-black ice lying jumbled around the edges of the polynya. He can see several automobile-sized chunks of ice floating in the clear, pale blue water.

Jellyfish, clear with faint, reddish stripes, float

slowly by the periscope. The captain backs the propeller just for an instant to check the very slight ship's motion.

The captain leans over to scan the polynya delineator. Its beam clearly traces the irregular outline of the polynya. The big pieces of ice are visible along with several more too far from the ship to make any difference.

Each of the upward-beam fathometer readings shows no ice above the ship. A check with the TV camera shows that all is clear overhead.

Now the trim pump begins to expel water from the auxiliary tanks amidships until the ship rises without a tremor.

With one last look around, the captain lowers his periscope. It would not do to have it damaged by an unobserved piece of ice. The sail planes fold in so that they will not be damaged. The stern planes will be deep down out of harm's way.

Up the submarine comes until the TV camera shows the top of the sail splash awash. Since no motion is felt inside the ship during the ascent, the halt is imperceptible. But the depth gauge shows that the correct depth has been reached for the sail to emerge. The needle on the gauge has ceased to move.

Carefully, just in case a piece of ice has lodged on top of the sail itself, the captain starts the periscope up. It is free, so he sends it rapidly up the rest of the way and puts his eye to the eyepiece.

A view of incredible beauty is his reward. Around the ship in all directions, as far as the eye can see, is a glistening, rugged expanse of beautiful white ice thrown up into a thousand shapes. The rays of the sun dance on the pack ice and reflect brilliantly from the dark blue surface of the open polynya.

"Surface!" orders the captain.

Air rushes into the main ballast tanks expelling the water. As the ship quivers and begins to rise, the air going to the after ballast tanks is shut off to keep the stern partly submerged for protection. The deck breaks water in a sudden cascade of water and foam.

In a few minutes sailors crowd the slippery deck looking in wonder at the frozen, apparently lifeless world about them. The summer temperature is not cold; the thermometer stands at 30° F. The submarine moves slowly to the edge of the polynya and moors with nylon mooring lines tied to steel stakes that the men drive into the ice.

The crew members not on watch go over on the ice. The crunchy ice crystals give good footing as the sailors tramp about inspecting the ends of tilted ice floes frozen in near-vertical positions under pressure from surrounding ice. So this is what the top of a pressure ridge looks like! Here and there are flat, smooth places as large as a living room, where the ice has actually melted in the sun's rays and then refrozen.

Scientific data must be obtained on each surfacing. Men are busy measuring the temperature of air and water, taking ice samples, and recording the many things that have to be studied to better understand the region. Inside the ship are reams of data which have been taken while the submarine was submerged.

Marine life is not neglected. The plankton sampler catches those tiny organisms in special nets. On surfacing, the nets are rushed below to the freezer. Because plankton is the basic food for many fish that in turn serve as food for larger fish and animals, the extent of life in the Arctic will not be fully known until we can chart the areas where plankton is thickest.

The navigator carefully shoots the sun to establish the exact position of the ship and to check the automatic instruments. A special kind of navigation is needed very near the North Pole because the compass direction north changes so rapidly as the submarine moves.

For example, a submarine that starts off heading *northeast* from a point 20 miles south of the Pole and moves in a *straight* line finds that she is heading due *east* by the time it passes by the Pole less than an hour later. Within another hour she will be heading *southeast*. And so a compass course is not good near the North Pole. A system to compensate for this has already been worked out and used by aircraft: the helmsman makes the frequent changes in the ship's compass heading needed to steer in a straight line.

Finally the rest period is over and the submarine drops into the depths to steam away on her mission. The crew knows that surfacings are not always as easy and enjoyable as that one.

Breaking through thick ice in the cold nighttime of winter is a more tricky operation. The periscope and television are useless. The ship has to burst through the ice. Once the sail has punched a hole, the sailors have to cut away the ice clogging the bridge in a temperature that may be minus 60° F. The air leaking down the bridge access trunk was so cold that a bucket of water froze in the *Sargo* control room.

Many of the men on board are unaware just how much the endless canopy of ice overhead weighs upon the subconscious mind until the hour arrives when the ship is free of the ice pack and on her way back to base. Then a sense of release and well-being floods over everyone. The mission has been successful!

The Arctic Ocean is a potential battleground for submarines because of its very inaccessibility. If an enemy put ballistic submarines off the Canadian archipelago, they could shoot down toward Canada and the United States. Such a patrol station for unfriendly missile submarines would mean just one thing: the United States Navy would have to keep submarines in the north to control the threat. By being first to move into the Arctic Ocean with its nuclear submarines and by keeping up its lead in exploration and operational experience, the United States Navy is making sure that it will be able to deal with any such threat.

14

THE INCREASING IMPORTANCE
OF SUBMARINES

THE NAVIES of the world have long sailed and fought on the surface of the oceans. The advantage of ducking briefly under the water and attacking from this hiding place has been apparent for even longer than the advantage of attacking from the air. What is fresh, and what is revolutionizing sea power, is the new-found means of operating continuously inside the ocean. Our present use of the submarine is novel enough, but the future promises far more radical changes and improvements.

After Symington in Scotland and Fulton in the United States invented the first practical steamboats at the beginning of the nineteenth century, there was a long period of hesitation and experiment before the steamship replaced the sailing ship. Today we look back on a great record achieved by steamships in war and peace—one that was only dimly foreseen 150 years ago. Can we look into the years ahead with enough imagination to see the future of the nuclear submarine?

So far the nuclear submarine has been too expensive and its technology too secret to have a commercial

A new anti-submarine weapon, the Subroc missile, will provide submarines with a means of killing other submarines at much greater ranges than torpedoes.

use. Whether it can be adapted to peaceful enterprises will depend largely on the success of improvements so costly that they can be financed only by the government. And the United States government is interested only in the military use of the submarine at present. The military use of submarines as hidden cargo carriers and troop transports may come, but the day when submarines are cheaper and better for such use seems remote indeed. For the present, nuclear power will be tried commercially only in the nuclear surface ship *Savannah*.

Yet the performance characteristics of the nuclear submarine warship are changing rapidly. New records for speed, diving depth, cruising range, size, or kill capability are posted almost every year. And these records have been set by making relatively minor changes in the submarine.

The fishlike hull shape and streamlining have given the submarine greater speed with the same horsepower. Increasing the thickness of the hull and putting more bracing on it have added to the diving depth. Improved reactor cores have increased the endurance of the submarine to give it several times the cruising range obtained with the first core of the *Nautilus*.

Minor improvements will continue to be made, transforming the nuclear submarine into a warship of peerless power. Major improvements may be still many years away.

The first major improvement needed, which is vital to both the Navy and the civilian ship lines, is the reduction of cost. It now costs over a hundred million dollars to build a Polaris submarine. An antisubmarine submarine costs about half that figure.

Reduction of cost is possible if the nation's shipyards modernize their procedures and use the latest mass production techniques. So many shipyards compete for the contracts to construct the small numbers of submarines that can be built annually that mass production is difficult. And the United States Navy itself is in a dilemma because the construction process is so slow. It takes about three years to build a submarine. By the end of that time important changes may be desirable, but it is terribly expensive to rip out equipment and start over.

Knowledgeable people in government and industry are sure that costs can be brought down, and there is a determined drive under way to carry through a comprehensive program of cost reduction. Even now, a commercial submarine without the expensive weapons and military requirements would be much less expensive to build than a warship, but it could not compete with the cost of a surface merchant ship.

The propulsion plant is another area in which significant improvements may one day be made. Our present steam plants are reliable and safe, and any substitute must be at least equally safe and reliable before it can be adopted. Many proposals have been advanced in recent years for the use of gas-cooled rather than water-cooled reactors in submarines, and for gas turbines instead of steam turbines.

Leading experts put such developments many years away unless the Atomic Energy Commission, which is working on these problems, comes up with some radically new ideas. Thus far the more efficient propulsion plants do not promise the safety and reliability of the present plants. The use of metallic sodium as a coolant was tried with moderate success in the second nuclear submarine, the *Seawolf*, but a leak and higher radioactivity made it necessary to shift to pressurized water.

The bathyscaphe *Trieste*, which set the record for deep diving, has shown that there is no practical limit to the operating depth of the submarine. Where the ordinary submarine now works at relatively shallow depths, within thirty years it may be working thousands of fathoms down.

The number of men needed to run our submarines today is only about one-fourth of the number needed to operate a surface warship of similar size. Even so, submarines of the future may operate with far fewer men if automation and simplified repair procedures are developed.

In present-day nuclear submarines the beautifully engineered reactor, requiring almost no servicing, is placed in a somewhat improved but conventional steamship engine room. Vice Admiral Rickover rightly resisted the desire of many enthusiastic designers to load the *Nautilus* and her successors with untried innovations. He had seen the result of expensive failures of radical designs all hooked together in the Navy's

unlucky destroyer USS *Timmerman*. He reportedly
felt that the *Nautilus* had a right to be a failure on the
basis of her reactor plant only.

As more experience is gained, the entire nuclear
submarine, from bow to stern, will become more efficient. Crews of forty-seven to seventy men will replace the present crews of twice that size. And as the
number of people drops, the size of the submarine
should tend to drop, too, and with it expense.

In weaponry we have hardly seen the beginning of
the submarine potential. The "intelligent" torpedo of
the future may be expected to locate a ship or submarine in the general vicinity of the point of aim,
regardless of sophisticated jamming or decoys. Only
the countertorpedo, destroying the attacking torpedo
in flight, would seem to promise an effective defense.

The submarine-launched missile is continuing its
spectacular development. In time it should be possible
to achieve accuracy in shore bombardment comparable
to that of a ship's guns in former years. How will the
leaders of the opposing navies use these improved
engines of war?

In a future war there might be battles fought by
squadrons of submerged submarines, maneuvered by
seagoing admirals intent on seizing the sea lanes of
the world. Control of the air has been necessary to
win recent battles on land and sea, and now control
of the inner ocean is indispensable for successful sea
warfare. In a war smaller than total hydrogen-bomb
warfare against whole populations, it is essential for
the Western world to control the seas so that we can

deploy our power against any aggressor. A battle of the future might go like this:

Cruising far submerged, the Blue fleet of thirty great antisubmarine submarines strung out in a long line of battle searches for the Green fleet. Far ahead the Green submarines are drawn up in a fixed defensive position. Each of them is circling slowly to minimize noise output and yet be sure to have steam ready to dash off at top speed. The Green submarines are stationed in a ring formation so that any enemy can be detected and fired upon no matter what his direction of approach is. An outer ring of sensitive sonar buoys has been planted on the bottom by the Green fleet to protect its position.

Suddenly a small Blue scout submarine passes over a buoy. The buoy reporting signal is cleverly masked and is unheard by the scout. Aboard the Green flagship, the admiral studies the buoy's report. An enemy stranger is coming in. Is it a scout for the Blue fleet, or is it a lone prowler? If it is a prowler it can be dispatched easily.

Steering by chance nearly straight for the Green fleet, the automatic brain of the robot Blue scout has received no inkling of the enemy. She slowly steams on to the "ping point." The Blue admiral had shrewdly calculated that by using a single, terrific sonar pulse the scout could illuminate the sea for 50 miles around her. Despite the noise of the lone scout, the exact position of the Blue fleet would still be unknown to the Green admiral.

"Ping!" goes the scout.

"Kill it!" orders the Green admiral in panic. But he is too late. His formation's position is revealed to a still invisible enemy.

The scout is dead; a great spout of radioactive water marks its destruction, and the terrible noise of the blast vibrates through the ocean, deafening Blue and Green alike. But the scout's sonar picture has been received in the Blue flagship and the exact position of the Green fleet is known by its enemy. The Blue fleet is ready to fire in seconds. Now it is the Blue admiral's turn to hesitate for an instant. The scout's sonar showed a great semicircle of twenty submarines. It did not see the submarines circling on the far side. The Blue admiral knows that the Greens have more submarines. Where is the rest of their fleet? Are they somewhere else just waiting for him to disclose his presence? Can they shoot fast enough to wipe him out?

"Commence firing. Execute Plan 7N," orders the Blue admiral. (Plan 7N is a scheme to scatter at top speed after firing, to launch decoys, and to reassemble at a prearranged point two hours later.)

The Green admiral is blown to the deck by the impact of the thirty exploding atomic warheads and rises shaken. So much noise is reverberating through the sea that communications and sonar are temporarily useless. He realizes as his head clears that his fleet has undoubtedly suffered grievously, but that he has at least his flagship intact and that probably more submarines escaped. A flash of insight comes to him. The Blues could see only part of his formation!

As the Green sonars return to normal, they can hear the Blue fleet moving at high speed to its new position. The Green admiral grins. His enemy does not realize how effective the Green sonar is. And the Green fleet still has twenty-two ships capable of action, although three are damaged. He sends a brief message designating targets.

"Commence firing!" orders the Green admiral grimly. The ocean erupts in a nightmare of towering pillars of radioactive steam. The Blue decoys have received part of the attack, but some Blue submarines are destroyed also.

But even before these explosions are triggered and

An artist's conception of an undersea fight between two nuclear-powered submarines.

while the missiles are in the air, the Blue submarines analyze the noise of the launching of the weapons and fire back at all twenty-two of the Green ships. It is a death blow to the Green fleet. Only a few fleeing Green submarines remain to be pursued by a detachment of Blue ships.

So might an underwater battle be fought. But by that time the nuclear submarine may be in full commercial use also.

Submarines will probably be used first as tankers, receiving and discharging their liquid cargo to pipelines run out from shore after the fashion of the huge surface supertankers today. A nuclear submarine passenger liner would be unequaled in speed and comfort —no rolling in the waves to cause seasickness, no fog delays or reduced speed because of storms. Service on time would be a hallmark of the nuclear submarine passenger liner.

In the depths the nuclear submarine may go treasure hunting, not for sunken hulls, but for mineral wealth: the oil, coal, gold, and other metals that are hidden in the bottom of the sea and that will have to be prospected when the world's land resources begin to be exhausted. This sea-bottom prospecting can go on even in the Arctic region where surface transportation has always been impossible. At any season submarines could visit underwater ports built where the water under the ice is deep enough for them to pass.

The possibility exists that submarines will be able to write new chapters in the history of fishing by using sonar to locate and control great schools of fish.

Will submarines one day tend underwater flocks of marine "cattle," bred especially for food value? The expanding population of the world may find this a way to feed itself.

The nuclear submarine has come into being so recently that we can be pardoned if we cannot yet imagine all its future uses. Those who man the submarines of the future will have to develop their full potential. It is their privilege and their challenge.